Cook for
Health, Healing & Vitality

Dr. Antonin Kodet, N.D., Paed. Dr.

www.drkodet.com

DISCLAIMER AND ADDITIONAL WARNING:

The purpose of this book is to educate readers with regards to the subject matter covered. It is sold with the understanding that the author, editors, contributors, publishers and any intermediaries are not liable for misconceptions or misuse of any information and recommendations. Extensive effort has been made to eliminate the potential for adverse reactions. The author, editors, contributors and publishers shall have neither liability nor responsibility to any person or entity with respect to any loss, damages, or injury caused or alleged to be caused by the information and/or recommendations in this book. **The information presented herein is in no way intended as a substitute for medical counseling.**

Regardless of the information presented, we encourage everyone to consult with their family physician before embarking on this or any other eating plan.

ACKNOWLEDGEMENTS

Many thanks to all not named below who selflessly tested my recipes, contributed their recipes and shared their experiences to make this book possible.

My appreciation goes to Joan Kennedy, Rob Grover and Wanda Posehn for testing recipes and providing their points of view.

I am especifically grateful to Liba Cunnings – the baker's daughter – who tirelessly baked, tested and perfected many of my recipes. She also helped with editing. I can't forget Sandra Auty, Rachael Pineau, Janice Kozlowski and Tiffany Self, who shared and tested recipes and lent their invaluable experience.

All contributors helped make this book a testament to the fact that natural, healthy, allergy-free nutrition need not be boring or bland.

I would also like to thank our unofficial panel of experts, specifically those who have more sensitive taste buds and less inhibitions with self-expression than us older folks. This includes those not old enough to talk (but capable of refusing anything they don't like to eat), right up to teens who never miss an opportunity to be heard.

Special thanks goes to Joan Dooling whose exceptional literary judgment and editing skills helped this book proceed.

I can not forget Sheena Archer and Shannon Harbour, whose tenacity in the production stage of this effort played a significant part in bringing all to completion.

My gratitude also goes to Elisa White for her long-standing support of this project, her key advice on concept and text, and the creative directing skills she applied to shape the look and feel of this book.

TABLE OF CONTENTS

FOREWORD

NOT ANOTHER HYPOALLERGENIC COOK BOOK

Although I originally wrote this book for those patients of mine whose culinary skills were marginal, the content is applicable to anyone – from the novice cook to the expert cook – who seeks a guideline to optimal health-building.

The focus is on health-nurturing meals that are simple and quick to prepare. The recipes allow for a variety of substitutions, so don't be dissuaded from giving a recipe a try just because you don't have all the ingredients on hand.

Seasoning amounts are reduced due to concerns about potential sensitivities or adverse reactions. Most recipes will work well even if some of the seasonings are omitted or substitutes are used. Feel free to adjust spices according to your taste preference and health condition.

Oil and butter use in my recipes is minimal. The goal is to accommodate those with a low tolerance to fat. However, I anticipate that some high energy readers or those who are 'slender-and-always-hungry', will increase the amount of fat to suit their needs.

Unless required for a specific reason, I do not advocate a low-fat diet. It is important to realize that people with sensitivities, allergies, chronic illnesses and increased levels of stress need to consume sufficient amounts of quality fats. The same applies to growing children and people recovering from illnesses or injuries. The right fats are required for energy and various vital functions in the body. Fat is also essential for adequate cholesterol production, the key to detoxification and hormone production.

Note: *The amount of water used in the cooking process may vary. More water is needed when:*

- *cooking for longer periods of time or at higher temperatures*
- *not covering the pot*
- *cooking at higher altitudes and in drier environments*
- *grains, beans and legumes are not soaked long enough*
- *you have a weaker digestive system (since it requires longer soaking and cooking times)*

SUCCESS FORMULA FOR THOSE STRESSED AND OVERWHELMED

1. **Relax!** Every great achievement starts with small steps.

2. **This is not a 'must-do-in-totality' regimen**. Remember, stress contributes to the development of allergies, hypersensitivities, digestive disorders, and other health problems. This book was written to put you on the path to healthy eating and should serve as a simple reference resource.

3. **Even a small change will help improve your recovery and optimize your overall performance.** I am consistently amazed by how much my patients improve even with only minor changes. This is particularly important for those whose health or life circumstances already are so overwhelming that they feel out control, fearful, and anxious.

4. **There is no time limit, no deadline and no exam so let go of performance anxiety and the stress that accompanies it.**

5. **Just pick a recipe and try it!** You don't need to be a seasoned cook or even have all the ingredients. Improvise with a recipe. Play with it. Enjoy the result. Your cooking knowledge and skills will improve as you progress.

6. **Make it easy on yourself.** For example, some people start by preparing one good meal per day, such as different grain porridge for breakfast. Others prefer to cook more on weekends. Change your eating habits at your own pace. You will be taking effective and important steps forward, whether you use a few or all of my recommendations.

7. **Have fun! Experiment with ingredients and foods you don't normally eat.** You'll be amazed at how easy it is to avoid eating the same foods day in and day out.

8. **Read the theory later.** Information contained in the crash courses is all you need to make a healthy meal. Remember, optimum health is a work in progress.

9. **Many of my patients see improvements within days.** How much and how quickly your health improves is proportional to your adherence to the program.

10. **Feel free to fall off the wagon – we all do that.** Just get back on again. This regimen is not intended to be a chore. Make it enjoyable. Improving your nutrition is an investment as well as a reward to yourself and to those who love you.

11. **Be patient.** Those who follow this eating regimen report acquiring a taste for the new foods while losing interest in less healthy alternatives. In addition, they grow accustomed to enjoying enhanced performance, better health and an overall feeling of well-being.

12. **The recipes in this collection are not only delicious, but are also easy to prepare.** Unlike many dietary programs, my recommendations don't sacrifice long-term health for short-term gain. The goal is sustained improvement in health, energy, vitality, performance and pain reduction.

Bon Appetît!

AN INTRODUCTION WORTH READING

1

WHO CAN BENEFIT?

"This program is designed to assist you in achieving the optimum health you deserve. Following my recommendations will help you to create a reality that includes psycho-emotional balance, appropriate weight, a radiant appearance and high levels of physical and mental performance and function." Dr. Antonin Kodet

THIS BOOK PROVIDES DIRECTION FOR THOSE WHO...

...CONSIDER THEMSELVES REASONABLY HEALTHY AND WISH TO:

- restore or develop a high level of energy and performance
- enhance and maintain intellectual functioning and psycho-emotional balance
- achieve athletic or other physical goals, dependent on optimal health, energy and performance
- maintain an active lifestyle while reducing stress levels
- achieve and maintain optimal health and weight
- rejuvenate their skin and aesthetic appeal
- practise preventative medicine

...ARE NOT ADEQUATELY HEALTHY AND WISH TO:

- achieve and maintain optimal health (physical and psycho-emotional)
- improve the quality of life and life expectancy
- maximize the effectiveness of conventional or natural treatments
- speed up and enhance recovery from various chronic illnesses, health conditions, injuries, surgeries and pain
- prepare for, or increase tolerance, to aggressive treatments and enhance post-treatment recovery (e.g. cancer treatments)

... HELP OTHERS WHO ARE NOT ADEQUATELY HEALTHY:

- health-care professionals helping patients
- parents attempting to improve the health and development of their children
- relatives whose loved ones have been stricken by illness or injury
- friends and volunteers trying to help others

❊ WHY TAKE CHARGE OF YOUR HEALTH?

The nutritional advice contained in this book is of crucial importance to those who are chronically ill or tired. It is also essential for busy people as well as high-achievers and athletes. While some readers may not be experiencing health or functional problems at this time, they may wish to start working on preventing or reversing potential chronic deficiencies now. This is because over time, chronic nutritional deficiencies will slowly and insidiously erode health and performance. However, anyone who lives or wishes to live an active life will benefit greatly from adopting sound nutritional habits. It is essential for our body to perpetually recuperate, adequately heal and consistently replenish its reserves. Prolonged depletion of reserves can result in chronic fatigue, reduced functional capacities and illnesses.

Many of my new patients happily claim that they already enjoy good health but wish to practise preventative strategies. Indeed, they are active individuals who eat according to what they believe are healthy guidelines. Often, I find that these patients are not enjoying nearly the level of health they are capable of achieving. When following my program, they report greater vitality than they thought possible. Ironically, most of them thought their aching muscles, memory lapses, fatigue and inability to concentrate, were natural consequences of getting older. In other words, they believed they were healthy except for the limitations imposed by their ageing bodies. On my regimen, they realized they can improve and ask much more from their bodies and mind.

> Many of my new patients happily claim that they already enjoy good health but wish to practise preventative strategies.

Another group of patients that continues to surprise me are my younger clients. After many years in practice, I am still amazed how quickly children improve or overcome their various illnesses and developmental deficiencies. Parents who help their children follow my nutritional regimen show them a healthy alternative to modern living. **This program provides parents with an invaluable tool to create a strong foundation of health for** **greater vitality, psycho-emotional balance, behaviour and intellectual function.**

I have used this nutritional regimen as the main component of my treatment programs for anyone from young children to competitive athletes. Whether the patient was struggling with ADD/ADHD, autism, allergies, asthma, chronic fatigue and fibromyalgia, colitis, Crohn's, IBS, digestive disorders, weight issues, infertility, auto-immune disorders or other severe chronic illnesses, the results spoke for themselves and were often beyond my patient's expectations.

Weight normalization is a natural outcome of the program and will occur even without focusing on achieving it. Improvement in functional capacities (digestion, absorption, detoxification, elimination, lymphatic function and self-regulation) leads to a reduction in the body's need to store fat. A poorly regulated and functioning body is in a state of nutritional deficiency and accumulates fat for energy reserves. A well-functioning and self-regulating body eliminates excessive fat. It also has expanded capacity to eliminate environmental toxins, metabolic by-products and fluids.

Correcting how internal organs function is important for rebuilding tissue. This is essential for those recovering from illnesses, injuries, surgeries and exhaustion, or for children and athletes.

Get the glow! Aesthetic improvement is a natural consequence of good health. While reducing or eliminating fluid retention, bloating and gas dramatically reduces the waist line, the most visible manifestation of internal improvement is in the skin. Here we see wrinkle reduction in addition to improved elasticity, texture and color.

While poor nutrition causes or contributes to the development of chronic illnesses, optimal nutrition plays a key role in their treatment. Essentially, recovery from all illness needs to include a supportive nutritional program. The same applies to treatment of intellectual, cognitive, psycho-emotional and behavioural disorders.

Naturopathic and Ayurvedic medicines are founded on the premise that specific foods can either disrupt function and damage various organs, or can improve function and help heal those same organs. Healthy organs support biochemical reactions essential to our intellectual, behavioral and emotional functioning. Deficient, poorly functioning organs have a reduced capacity to do so. Traditional Chinese Medicine (TCM) confirms this theory.

TCM teaches that an abnormal emotion originates with a dysfunction in a specific organ. Some examples of organ to emotion coupling are:

* Liver – anger (a poorly performing liver increases propensity for anger)
* Kidneys – fear (damaged kidneys lead to fearfulness)
* Lungs – grief (diseased lungs create grief)

* Spleen – pensiveness (a 'damp' or poorly functioning spleen can lead to states of over-introspection)

In fact, TCM treats emotions by treating their associated organs. This approach is reflected in my recommendations as well. I am providing nutritional guidelines to help poorly functioning organs which in turn, improves their emotional counterparts.

Another understated fact is the influence of food choices on pain reduction. For the record, I wish to confirm that my proposed nutritional regimen can substantially reduce pain. Many of my patients report a dramatic reduction in pain and discomfort within weeks or even days of following my treatment program.

Poor food choices can lead to a series of adverse events:

* Aggravating foods cause irritation in various organs and glands, primarily those involved in digestion, absorption and elimination
* Prolonged irritation of these organs leads to increased inflammation and inflammation produces pain
* Inflammation is managed by the immune system; when the immune system is diverted from other parts of the body to focus on digestion, absorption and elimination, it becomes overloaded

We experience that overload as pain or discomfort in our abdomen, joints, muscles or other parts of our body. These are the body's warning signs indicating that harm has been done to our body and we need to make appropriate changes to correct it. It is important to realize that a perpetually poor diet leads to chronic inflammation and ultimately to a chronic condition characterized by persistent pain.

The solution is simple: Incorporate the dietary advice in this book into your daily eating regime and reduce the insults to your system. Eating the right foods will reduce digestive irritation which in turn reduces inflammation and pain. Less inflammation lowers the demands on the immune system allowing it to focus on healing and protecting. The immune system and other organs can now clean up, rebuild and function without being pushed to their limits. Radiant health ensues.

I need to stress that our health is primarily our responsibility and the nutritional choices we make are *entirely* up to us. Frankly, our medical and economic systems are not designed to prevent illness or enhance health. Rather, they are driven by the business of sickness. A friend of mine, an experienced medical doctor, once stated that we should replace the title *Ministry of Health and Wellness* by the *Ministry of Sickness*.

We should critically examine what is written and said about healthy eating keeping in mind that even **regulatory agencies are not immune to commercial interests. In addition, those who design and maintain the 'gold standard of medicine' have little or no training in the effective use of nutrition in the treatment and prevention of pain or disease.**

It is clear that the burden of making correct decisions regarding our nutrition is entirely up to us. We have the capability, choice and opportunity to make independent decisions. Regrettably, instead of struggling for logical analysis of available facts in the nutritional arena, many of us still tend to look for solutions based on dependence. In my opinion, we hand over important health-related decisions to those with the ultimate objective of increasing their profit margins.

And, when pills, injections or fad diets cease to work, many of us accept various states of fatigue, illness and inactivity as our destiny. All of these outcomes can be improved when we take steps to make our own decisions with regards to nutrition. We <u>can</u> reclaim our health and enjoy lasting vitality.

Look around. Do you know people who abandoned their ambitions and goals for health reasons? How many of us think this is inevitable as we weaken with disease or age? It doesn't have to be. While I am aware there are adverse environmental, social and other pressures, it still stands that achieving optimum health and function is well within our power. Making these dreams a reality is not as overwhelming as some of us may think.

Our goals are personal and so are our starting points, expectations and needs. Optimum health must be defined differently for each of us because we are individuals with unique sets of characteristics. Nonetheless, all of us can make meaningful changes to achieve optimum health and performance. No matter what your starting point, correct nutrition is one of the main factors in building a healthier, more enjoyable and satisfying life.

Our body is designed to heal itself but it needs correct conditions to do so. Pain, perpetual fatigue, chronic illnesses or low functional capacities can be resolved or at least improved with correct nutrition.

There is no need to stress about various details of the program. Just start where and when it makes sense for you. Take it full speed or bit by bit. Beginnings are always harder. Just persevere to make optimum health and a highly satisfying life your reality.

Correct nutrition is required for any effective treatment, rehabilitation, post-treatment recovery or exercise program. The goal of this book is to equip you with the information you need to assume a more effective and healthier nutritional approach to your life. However, this or any other book or guide is not a substitute for the treatment or coaching offered by highly qualified, competent and experienced health care providers.

I would specifically like to reference competent, licensed naturopathic physicians, health professionals often referred to as 'North America's Best Kept Secret'.

On this continent, naturopathic physicians are the medical professionals best qualified to use nutrition for therapeutic purposes. They are trained and qualified to diagnose and treat independently or in conjunction with relevant specialists as required. Naturopathic medical schools provide rigorous training in conventional medical sciences and therapeutic modalities *as well as* in natural therapies. This is why the duration of naturopathic medical school programs are longer than their conventional counterparts. In addition to conventional medical science, they teach herbal medicine, homeopathy, hydrotherapy, musculoskeletal manipulation, nutritional therapy and other natural treatments.

Depending on state or provincial regulations, naturopathic physicians may be licensed to perform minor surgeries and prescribe conventional medications. This is why naturopathic physicians are often thought of as a bridge between natural and conventional medicine. They can safely and effectively treat those who prefer natural treatments, as well as those who are concurrently treated conventionally.

Access to both worlds, natural and conventional, provides a safer and more effective alternative than either system alone, and is certainly preferable to self-diagnosis and self-treatment. Nobody is perfectly healthy or omniscient – just find the right physician for your philosophy and health condition.

Most of us who have some interest in nutrition believe that we eat reasonably well. We also tend to agree that good nutrition, digestion and elimination are necessary to good health. So why are we becoming sicker and weaker?

" During medical school, I had the great fortune of meeting Dr. Kodet and subsequently, becoming his patient. He treated me consistently throughout the four years of my studies. Using various forms of manipulation and rehabilitative techniques, he enabled me to keep up with the tremendous demands of the program despite my physical limitations resulting from polio infection. I continue to search for one so capable, talented and skillful as we are miles apart now. "

– Dr. Julie Forbes

❊ NO SUCH THING AS 'ONE DIET FITS ALL'

I think we have been coached to regard the Canada Food Guide or the U.S. Daily Recommended Food Allowances as nutritional bibles. Unfortunately, no nutritional guide is perfect. In fact, both conventional and alternative medical professionals recognize many deficiencies in both of these North American guides.

1. Food guides are not designed to promote consumption of a wide variety of foods. In fact, they focus on a relatively restricted number of foods. For example, bread, pasta, pancakes, muffins, cakes, pastries and pizza are all made from wheat. Milk, yogurt and cheese are all dairy products. Lower dietary variety leads to nutritional deficiencies and an increased propensity to develop food sensitivities, allergies and chronic illnesses. This lack of diversity can also cause reduced performance levels and reduced capacity to recuperate.

2. Both guides recommend consuming some of the most allergenic and irritating foods as diet staples. These foods can either directly aggravate or contribute to the aggravation and damage of our bodily organs. Restricted food choices and the inclusion of allergenic and irritating foods have been linked to the increased proliferation of modern illnesses and the reduction of our functional capacities. Additionally, they negatively affect sexual performance, sleep, resistance to fatigue and illnesses, thought clarity and behaviour. Coincidentally, some of the foods we are told to extensively consume are produced in excess in Canada and the U.S.

3. There is an apparent disregard for our ability to digest, absorb, benefit from, and eliminate various foods. The guides erroneously suggest that what is consumed is also effectively absorbed and used. However, this assumption is contrary to the ancient knowledge inherent to doctors of Oriental, Ayurvedic and Naturopathic medicines. These time-honoured systems are based on the understanding that even foods with highly desirable constituents can be harmful to our health and that how we prepare and consume our food is as important as what we eat.

Over the years, I have treated many patients who arrived at my practice after trying numerous diets. Based on my work with them, my opinion is that an overwhelming majority of modern western diets have not been beneficial in the long run. In fact, some of these diets contribute to the development of obesity, poor energy and performance, and chronic illnesses including cancer and even death.

I have studied nutrition on several continents. This includes formal studies at post-secondary institutions as well as field observations focused on determining the impact of local nutrition on human development, function and health.

4. There is no question in my mind that the relationship between diet and health is staggering. Clearly, the evidence that the food we consume has a major effect on us – either detrimental or curative – is overwhelming. Of course this is not limited to North America and Western Europe. The standard American diet is negatively affecting health in developing countries where the population is wealthy enough to afford the fast or processed food that so characterizes our North American diet. Those in poor countries tend to regard western foods as status symbols.

During my work abroad, it was quite obvious that those who ate the standard American diet became more obese, ill and less vital. I have observed such changes in less time than a decade! Laypeople and researchers alike confirm my findings. I can attest that those who maintained their traditional natural diet were healthier than those who did not. I routinely see how food dramatically improves a patient's condition when all other treatments fail.

I can't resist mentioning two indelible profiles from my travels:

The first one is of a boy whose parents operated a kiosk high in the mountains of India. The boy was enjoying a higher status among other children because he was given various western snack bars. His other environmental and social conditions were comparable to the majority of local children in that they all lived in mountain huts that were inaccessible even by Land Rover. Although these kids appeared exceptionally strong and healthy, the boy with the candy bars was the only one with large skin lesions on his head, consistent with psoriasis.

The other example is of a family in southern Panama. The youngest of the family had severely deteriorated teeth. She was clearly the favourite in the family and as such, was given Western-type treats. The older children had good teeth, were slim, strong and carried their own bags. The mother had perfect teeth, was strong and at her ideal weight. She was carrying this obese toddler and the rest of the baggage, although the toddler could have walked. They lived in a hut in a half-jungle, half-agrarian region.

5. There is no universally accepted dogma or opinion concerning nutritional systems, nor any bullet-proof research findings. It seems that fashion and finance are the mo-tivators, not facts. This is one of the reasons why I frequently consult old medicines, especially Oriental and Ayurvedic, for answers. Both of these medicines have had thousands of years to test their theories and methods. In writing this book I was also sensitive to recommendations and assumptions made by other dietary systems from paleontological to vegetarian and microbiotic.

The recommendations in this cookbook are based either on research findings that made sense or on easily applicable teachings from other medicines. The knowledge from Oriental, Ayurvedic, and to some extent, macrobiotic medicines had to be Westernized. In addition, the old teachings had to be adapted to our modern illnesses and health conditions. Needless to say, the information concurs with the teachings of Naturopathic medicine and is validated by modern research.

Over the years, I have used a variety of dietary regimens to treat a broad spectrum of people, from the severely ill to healthy competitive athletes. This practice has revealed the strengths and limitations of various diets. It also allowed me to identify positive features from these diets that produced the best and most consistent results. I have gradually formulated everything I learned into a comprehensive set of nutritional recommendations and recipes. I then tested, revised and retested them. The results are contained within this book.

6. Combining approaches helped overcome deficiencies inherent to any single diet. It proved to be a key factor in restoring and optimizing health, energy and performance, while correcting weight on a short-term as well as a long-term basis.

Of course, there is a very strong correlation between the magnitude of improvements and the degree of adherence to these recommendations. Patients and athletes who followed my advice diligently improved more than those who did not.

7. The recommendations contained within this book do not constitute a 'diet' and are not carved in stone. What I propose are merely nutritional strategies that can be incorporated into anyone's nutritional regimen regardless of what that regimen looks like to start.

Basic rule of thumb: The more ill or more sensitive a person is, the more closely he or she should follow the recommendations outlined in this book, at least until solid improvements are seen and adequate reserves are built up.

Although I have not imposed limits on the amount of food consumed, the old 'eat until half full' remains the best advice. Athletes, children and those with high nutritional needs have to eat enough to meet their requirements. But do not overeat. Overeating strains all the involved systems and reduces the capacity to recover and recuperate.

I am aware that some of the opinions presented here will not correspond with those stated in various nutritional magazines, health books and the more or less official food guides. Please bear in mind that there is overwhelming evidence to suggest that our North American diet has been the primary cause of a catastrophic proliferation of chronic illnesses.

Consider for example that cancer is now the biggest killer of children over the age of five. Also, note that immigrants to this continent develop our common chronic illnesses when they adopt our nutritional habits. This is notwithstanding the fact that there is no historical link to these ailments in their country of origin. Actually, people do not even have to

relocate here. Consuming the standard American diet is enough to cause these illnesses, regardless of where one lives.

It may come as a surprise but studies indicate that longevity in poor developing countries is now comparable to ours. However, their senior citizens are generally more functional than ours. Remember that these developing countries do not receive much medical care or medication. However, they consume their traditional diet.

Let me provide one more example of diet-induced calamity. Around twenty years ago in Playa del Carmen, south of Cancun, Mexico, I had breakfast with the locals. On the menu that day was grouper – caught that morning and roasted over a natural fire – with fresh handmade tortillas seasoned with a bit of coarse salt. The fisherman's wife served it on a bamboo leaf, right out of the wheelbarrow she brought it in. The fish was gone before it even cooled down. I also bought a coconut and some fresh fruit from street vendors. It was a delicious, dirt-cheap breakfast – full of nutrients and fabulous taste – and it left me feeling great afterward. The locals were friendly, happy, slim and energetic.

Five years ago I visited the same place again. The village had become a significant tourist centre and I was shocked by the overall size of the locals I saw in the streets. The old-style vendors were gone; fast food in styrofoam boxes was in. There were obvious signs that this society was leaning toward the same fate as fellow Hispanics who had immigrated to the U.S. – that is, increased propensity towards obesity, diabetes, cardiovascular disease and other illnesses.

I would also like to reiterate that the majority of the world population is still treated by complementary and alternative medicines. In fact, even in the U.S., a growing number of people are choosing to take proactive steps and returning to alternative medicine.

8. Recent data indicates that in the U.S. visits to alternative medicine providers EXCEED those made to MDs by 40 percent. Historically, effective and no-nonsense nutritional programs have been the foundation of any natural treatment protocol. Doctoral-level practitioners of natural medicine are extensively trained in therapeutic nutrition and their patients should expect to receive nutritional guidelines and support.

I have been in many locations around the world where people had only very limited access to alternative medicine or no access to *any* medical system, conventional or alternative. However, the local people had a highly practical and applicable understanding of how to use food to facilitate the healing process and improve health. Not surprisingly, they were healthy and rarely became ill. I do acknowledge that there were other factors involved, but when Western food moved in, their health started to dramatically deteriorate.

If you'd like an example from our own North American backyards, consider this: several years ago, a patient told me that her grandparents observed a critical deterioration in the health of the aboriginal population *within five years* of switching from a Native to a Western diet. I wasn't surprised. The elders advised against eating our highly processed food blaming it for eveything from general weakness to tooth loss. By the way, there are theories and evidence supporting the concept that non-Native food devastated the aboriginals more than the introduction of alcohol.

Although my proposed dietary regimen might initially pose a significant challenge for some, it is not very difficult to follow once you be-

come accustomed to it. My intention is to give you a starting point from which to build your own personalized nutritional system. Most people choose to follow this program more closely when they are recovering from an illness, when rebuilding their energy or when maximizing their athletic performance. They then deviate from it when their health and performance are better. Others choose strategies that can be most easily incorporated into their existing nutritional approach and lifestyle.

Consider the effort you put forth as an investment in your health and in the health of your family. Know that this investment will improve the quality of life for you and those you love.

Note: *Since it is impossible to cover everything in one small cookbook, my next book will expand on some of the reasons for my nutritional advice. It will also provide additional explanations and recommendations on how to maximize your recovery from a chronic illness, improve your health and increase your energy and performance.*

FOUNDATION STONES OF HEALTH

Simply stated, my approach combines the benefits of several different dietary regimens that share the same health improvement goals. These include **Hypoallergenic, Elimination, Diversified, Rotational, Organic** and **Natural** diets. To a limited extent I have also considered some of the advice specified in **Blood Type Specific** Diet (as presented by Doctors D'Adamo, N.D. in their book *Eat Right for Your Type.*).

BREAKING IT DOWN: HOW AND WHY EACH APPROACH WORKS

The **HYPOALLERGENIC** diet consists of foods that are less likely to produce allergic or sensitivity reactions or aggravate the digestive system. Foods that are known or suspected to produce allergic or sensitivity reactions (dairy, wheat, etc) are excluded from the hypoallergenic diet.

The **ELIMINATION** diet excludes all foods inclined to trigger sensitivity and intolerance reactions within our bodies. It also eliminates foods causing other adverse reations. For example, vegetables in the nightshade family (potatoes, tomatoes, peppers, eggplant) are eliminated. All foods that have a high potential to aggravate your system or negatively impact your energy level are eliminated.

The **DIVERSIFIED** diet advocates incorporating a broad variety of foods not usually included in our diet. New foods are also used to replace any offending foods. The more sensitive the person is, the more diversified and exotic the food choices need to be. The goal is to introduce more high-value foods that tend to be well tolerated. Greater variety translates into a broader range of macro-nutrients and micro-nutrients in our diet, less irritation and lower propensity to auto-immune reactions. This means fewer deficiencies and a healthier diet overall.

The **ROTATIONAL** diet requires us to rotate the foods that we tend to most often consume. Each food can potentially become an allergen or produce adverse reactions, especially if we eat a single food consistently or excessively. The rotational diet directs us to eat a particular food only once every four or more days. The goal is to give the body a break from a particular food to keep from over-reacting to it.

The **NATURAL** diet requires exclusion of all food which has been irradiated, processed, chemically preserved or otherwise altered. This includes junk food, fast food, canned goods and irradiated spices.

The **ORGANIC** diet proposes eating organically or at least naturally grown foods. These foods typically contain less toxic, irritating and otherwise harmful substances than their non-organic counterparts. In addition, the amount of GMO (genetically modified) foods should be reduced. The result will be cleaner food, increased nutritional value and better taste.

The **BLOOD TYPE SPECIFIC** diet, most recently written about by Doctors D'Adamo, father and son, stems from the presence of cell surface sugars called lectins. These are specific to different foods and depending on your blood type, can produce adverse reactions. Many key recommendations of the blood type diet are consistent with findings of the ancient medicines and have already been incorporated into my regimen.

The main lessons that we should learn from Doctors D'Adamo are those people with blood type:

✦ **O** do best with meat and vegetables and should not overdo grains and beans.

✦ **A** do not do well with meat and should refrain from eating eggs and the meat of larger animals. They do well with beans, grains and vegetables.

✦ **B** do better with lamb, mutton, venison, rabbit and fish, and can consume other meats except for chicken. They can adapt to higher or lower consumption of meat, but should grind grains and cook sprouts. May have to eliminate or reduce consumption of some nuts and seeds.

✦ **AB** carry features of both A and B types and have to consider both of them. For example AB should have a better capacity to tolerate meat than A, but worse capacity than B.

Note: *The extent of how organic the food actually is will depend on where your organic food comes from and who produces it. In general, 'natural' does not meet the criteria of being certified organic, although you may find farmers or ranchers whose natural food may be far superior to organic. Usually this is because they produced it organically but did not bother with the certification process. Make it a practice to shop around. You may find some organic foods at prices comparable to conventionally produced foods.*

Note: *If the food is listed in my "Foods to Avoid List" or if you find it aggravating, it is imperative to eliminate it regardless of whether it is considered beneficial to your blood type or not.*

Note: *Again, the more ill or sensitive the person is, the more diligently they need to follow my recommendations.*

WISDOM VERSUS COMMON DOGMA (COOKED FOODS VERSUS RAW FOODS)

Believe it or not, most populous world cultures cook almost all food, including what we would consider salad-type vegetables.

I can already hear the uproar to my suggestion that <u>all</u> food should be cooked. Aren't you a doctor? Doctors are supposed to know that raw salads can potentially cure everything from bunions and cancer to insanity!

Granted, I may have developed a bias based on what I have observed in my practice. Those who come to see me don't seem to benefit from the raw food diet in the long term. That said, the benefits and drawbacks of cooked foods are not new topics for the scientific community studying nutrition. Unfortunately for the general public, **science needs to be financed, and unless there is a promise of financial gain, there is little incentive to dispel nutritional myths**.

One of the main differences between what you read here and elsewhere is my advice to:

1. Cook essentially all, or at least most, of your foods

2. Consume them warm

This advice is consistent with the teachings of Oriental and Ayurvedic medicines. Their recommendations are based on thousands of years of observation that raw vegetables and fruits are too cooling and dampening for our digestive system. Based on their teachings, a cold and damp digestive system can't extract nutrients effectively and therefore produces an excess of by-products. They also state that raw vegetables are too rough for your digestive system and are harder to break down than cooked vegetables.

Modern medical science confirms that digestion is the work of enzymes and intestinal bacteria. These do not work properly if the digestive temperature is too low. When we eat raw food that is cold and has cooling characteristics, we absorb fewer nutrients and end up converting more of the good foods to toxins and allergens.

Along the same line, cooking deactivates goitrogens – substances which suppress the production of the thyroid hormone. The thyroid hormone helps maintain the appropriate temperature when digesting. If digestion is too cold, our digestive enzymes will not work effectively. That is why we refrigerate our food – to slow down the work of the enzymes within it, delaying its breakdown. Goitrogen-containing foods include: peanuts, soybeans, broccoli, cabbage, cauliflower, kale, turnips, millet, pine nuts, cassava root and mustard. Make certain you cook these foods. This is especially crucial for those suffering with hypothyroidism or sub-clinical hypothyroidism.

There is another important reason why modern nutritional science confirms that our ancestors were correct in processing their food by heating it. **Grains, legumes and seeds contain substances such as phytates, oxalates, tannins, saponins and other elements occasionally referred to as anti-nutrients.** These reduce our capacity to break down proteins and to absorb minerals such as calcium, iron, magnesium, phosphorus, zinc and proteins. The phytates and other so-called anti-nutrients are destroyed by cooking, baking, soaking, sprouting, fermenting, and other forms of processing, allowing us to digest more minerals and proteins.

The method of heating food is also a factor in this equation. For example, baking vegetables does not reduce their oxalate content while boiling them does. During boiling, the oxalates escape into the water and evaporate. The elimination of oxalates from food is important since there are concerns that oxalates reduce calcium absorption and increase the propensity for the development of calcium oxalate kidney stones. Some kidney stones are formed from calcium oxalate.

Research also confirms that cooking vegetables is not as detrimental to their nutrient content as many of us were led to believe. However, it is important not to overcook them; instead, consider brief steaming or stir-frying. It is important to bring water to a boil before steaming or boiling vegetables.

Because our digestive systems do not produce enzymes to break down fibers like cellulose, cooking becomes a critical part of the process.

In addition, cooking tends to destroy microbial agents, thereby improving our protection from microbial contamination. It is important to consider that mass-produced food remains quite vulnerable to microbial contamination in spite of extensive government regulations.

Both Oriental and Ayurvedic medicine recommend refraining from using leftovers or reheating foods. Their explanation is that cold food is stale, cooling and dampening and should be avoided. According to Chinese medicine, coldness and dampness hamper digestive transformation. Those with sensitive digestive systems would agree. Leftovers are disturbing to our digestive, absorptive, immune and other systems. Our enzymes and

intestinal bacteria require an elevated temperature to digest effectively. The cooling and dampening effect of leftovers reduces the digestive temperature. Relatively few of us are aware that vitamins are destroyed, not only by cooking and various forms of processing, but also by cooling. In fact, in terms of their residual vitamin content, cooked vegetables can be thrown out after a few hours of being allowed to cool down. Cooking with leftovers means using aggravating foods with minimal nutritional content.

✳ MEAT AND HEAT

There are numerous studies indicating that carcinogenic substances such as heterocyclic amines and aromatic hydrocarbons are produced when cooking meat. This is made worse with a combination of high temperatures and prolonged cooking times.

Rule of thumb: use low heat when cooking and don't overcook meat. Boil, steam, poach and braise at temperatures less than 210ºF (100ºC). Bake and roast at temperatures no higher than 390ºF (200ºC). These are better choices than barbecuing, broiling, grilling or pan-frying methods that have exceedingly high cooking temperatures. If you must use the high-heat forms of cooking, try to reduce the heat and keep the meat away from the flames. Do not consume any charred meat. Cured and smoked meat also contain carcinogenic substances.

My impression is that life is a balancing act. On one side, we are continuously exposed to carcinogenic and other harmful substances, natural or synthetic. On the other side, we have the capacity to reduce our exposure to carcinogens. It is up to us to decide to what extent we are prepared to alter our lifestyle and nutritional habits for our heath.

❈ VEGETABLES AND THEIR RAW IMPACT

Imagine a weak, irritated and inflamed digestive tract that has to process hard- and rough-textured vegetables.

Eating raw, hard-textured vegetables irritates a sensitive stomach and isn't any kinder to your intestines. When this happens, the fiber does not get broken down well enough for the digestive enzymes to penetrate it and do their job properly. In more severe cases, the digestive system either will eliminate the food via diarrhea or struggle to work with it, making it sluggish and plugged up. Depending on the severity of the irritation, we may experience a variety of symptoms: spasm with diarrhea, severe constipation, softer or harder stools, undigested food pieces, gas, bloating, burping, body odour, gastro esophageal reflux and pain.

Logically, those of us who have 'a baby's stomach' have to cook as though for an infant. Cooked vegetables are softer for irritated or inflamed digestive tissues than raw vegetables. A cold digestive system has to be warmed up to help with digestion. One suggestion is to drink a cup of warm tea a few minutes before eating, and then eat your food warm.

This advice is more critical in cool climates and for those of us who tend to be physically cold. Again, remember that we refrigerate our food to slow down the digestive action of the enzymes within it.

Those with stronger digestive systems can eat a small amount of raw vegetables as long as they are of the softer variety.

❈ JUICING AND THE INSULIN CONNECTION

It's reasonable to assume that juicing fruits and vegetables would be highly beneficial for our health since it breaks down fibre. Not so. In fact, juicing elimiates fibre while increasing sweetness. In addition, raw fruits and vegetables have a cooling and dampening effect on the digestion. **Remember that a sweet taste, not just the presence of simple sugars, triggers the release of insulin. Excessive insulin leads to greater energy fluctuations and hypoglycemia, as well as to an increased conversion of carbohydrates to fats.**

Dr. Harold Dick, N.D., who is still considered an icon of naturopathic medicine, routinely treated illnesses considered incurable by conventional means. He felt that it did not make sense to give a patient a glass of juice made from five apples if the patient did not have the capacity to eat five apples. Oriental and Ayurvedic medicine would agree with him. In addition to all the arguments stated above, they considered juices excessively nutritious and too overwhelming for digestive absorption.

❈ FILLING THE GAP WITH SUPPLEMENTS

Sensitive people have to be more cautious about using supplements. Some supplements can aid in recovery, but their prescription has to make sense. Remember, supplements can irritate and produce allergic or even anaphylactic reactions. Make no mistake – some supplements also contain toxic residues and other by-products. Most people do not adequately digest and absorb supplements anyway.

Furthermore, if we provide the body with anything in excess, the body has to take two corrective actions:

1. Eliminate the excess, that:
   - creates more work for the liver, kidneys, digestion, glands, lymphatic and immune systems
   - temporarily reduces our capacity to fight toxins and harmful microbial agents

2. Reduce the production of digestive enzymes required to extract the nutrients from the supplements and food. This means the body will be absorbing fewer nutrients from the food and the supplements as well as producing more potentially irritating by-products which have to be processed and eliminated.

" My life has been characterized by violence along with the stress and illness that accompany it. I suffered the tragic loss of my children, endured family abuse and survived three severe vehicular accidents. With the pain I was experiencing, I couldn't see a future for myself. I would have preferred to die. I experienced severe insomnia, nightmares, chronic muscle and back pain, abdominal pain, headaches, depression, lack of concentration and poor short-term memory. I also had hearing and vision problems.

Dr. Kodet helped me to either resolve the ailments or considerably reduce the symptoms around them. His treatment also helped to save one of my organs and avoid surgery. I've come a long way and now am grateful for my new life. I look forward to the future.

I work in the health care field and have referred many patients to Dr. Kodet. All those who followed his advice either recovered or improved. My advice to readers is not to think of the proposed nutritional change as an overwhelming chore. It's really about upgrading from our learned deprivation mode to a creative cooking style that offers more opportunities for a healthy life. "

– L. Cunnings (Registered Massage Therapist, RMT)

COOKING METHODOLOGY 101

4

There are various philosophies concerning how long and at what temperature we should cook our food.

HIGH AND FAST OR LOW AND SLOW?

Some, but not all, conventional Western medical thinking appears to favour higher heat for a shorter period of time. This rationale condemns slow cooking as the worst method for preservation of food value. This is also consistent with opinions presented by Oriental medicine that advocates fast, high-heat cooking.

The teachings of Ayurvedic medicine, which are also based on thousands of years of experience, stress slow cooking at low heat for long periods of time. The research supporting this view is becoming more prevalent and more widely accepted.

As with anything else concerning nutrition, there are proponents and opponents alike. Each can back up their opinions by using more or less convincing scientific evidence that supports their unique views.

■ **SLOW COOKING:** My impression is that slow cookers or crock pots are very handy and easy to use. Just throw the ingredients in the slow cooker in the morning, turn it on, and dinner is ready in the evening. If you are concerned about the potential for loss of vitamins, try this option: cook the beans and grains in the slow cooker and use a fast-cooking method for your vegetables and meats at the end of your cooking.

■ **PRESSURE COOKING:** For those who are more ill, or have weak digestive systems, overcooking is necessary in the initial stages of recovery.

Slow cooking can take several hours. Pressure or high-heat cooking is usually more convenient. This is especially important when cooking soup bones, beans and grains that take longer to cook. Pressure cooking and stir-frying reduce the time needed for cooking and save energy. In addition, microbial agents do not stand a chance of surviving the rapid changes inherent to pressure cooking. I have seen ordinary pressure cookers being used for sterilization of surgical equipment in Third World hospitals. This includes equipment for eye surgeries.

Using a pressure cooker not only saves time and energy, but it may also reduce the destruction of vitamins when compared to other higher heat cooking methods. This is because it dramatically reduces cooking time and consequently the food's exposure to high heat.

Note: Since pressure cookers differ from each other in terms of water usage and pressure settings, please consult your user's manual for best results. The recipes that follow provide general directions only. In addition, please consult the manufacturer's recommendations concerning the safe use of your pressure cooker.

■ **STIR-FRYING** is sometimes frowned upon because of the potential of the high heat to damage fats. My opinion is that fat damage can be dramatically reduced if we use the correct techniques and ingredients (see the Crash Course in Stir-Frying).

■ **BOILING** is a self-explanatory cooking method. Later in this book I will comment on which foods are best started in cold water as opposed to being added to boiling water – the most common approach.

■ **BAKING** is the cooking method that many of my patients find too intimidating or time-consuming, although neither has to be the case.

■ **BRAISING** employs moist heat and is used primarily for meat preparation especially when cheaper, tougher cuts (such as ribs) are on the menu. Braising is usually done with low heat over a long period of time – several hours (see the Crash Course in Braising).

■ **POACHING** involves slipping the food into a small amount of gently boiling water and cooking it without allowing the food to disperse. Poaching is often used for eggs. Some people favour poaching cups for eggs, which involves partially immersing the metal cups in a water bath. Fish also poaches well.

■ **STEAMING** cooks the food over the steam generated by boiling water. Steamers are as widely varied as they are available.

> ### Note:
> **Damage to Fats:** *The least controversial approach to avoiding heat damage to fat is to boil, bake, braise, poach or steam your food. If the food does not have enough fat of its own, healthy fats or oils should be added either at the* completion *of cooking or* when serving.

"Where do you go after you have been through nine doctors, both conventional and naturopathic? When I met Dr. Kodet, I had been diagnosed with heavy metal toxicity which had eroded my nervous system and organs and depleted my body. Today, I am energetic, pain-free, happy and alert. In fact, it has been more than 10 years since I have felt this good.

But, it took me eight years to find a doctor who I could relate to so well. There are many things that make Dr. Kodet a good doctor. However, the one thing that makes him exceptional, truly exceptional – is the depth of his understanding of you as an individual with an illness. He knows what road map to give that 'whole individual' to lead a healthy life. You can't find that ability in a medical textbook. It is obvious that some are clearly born to be doctors.

For those of you wondering what step to take next, I recommend calling Dr. Kodet. When you do not even understand yourself, when you are too tired or sick to try any longer, he will come up with a plan and guide you back to a healthy state."

– Wanda Posehn

❋ THE NUANCES OF HEALTHY EATING HABITS

Believe it or not, where, when, in what form and how you consume your food is very important.

Eat only:

- at the same times every day
- while sitting down as opposed to standing up, or, even worse, walking, running, driving...
- consistently-sized meals (do not have one big meal that would induce you to skip the following meal)
- when the desire comes from your body, not your mind
- only when you are naturally hungry
- when your stomach has finished digesting your previous snack or meal
- an appropriate amount – do not over-eat or under-eat
- wholesome foods, organic or natural if possible
- in congenial company or in silence

Do not eat when:

- angry, upset, worried or depressed (hence the term 'comfort foods')
- watching TV, reading, listening to the radio or talking on the phone
- drinking cold beverages
- hunger is satiated (stop before you have had enough and your 'full receptor' will catch up in about 15 minutes)

> **Remember:** *Your vitality depends on your digestion.*

Tips about drinking while eating:

- it is ideal to drink a cup of warm tea or water before eating (recall that this is what they first bring you in Chinese restaurants)
- do not drink during or after meals. If you must, have a small cup of tea during or after meals (wine or beer can be taken during or after meals if the occasion calls for it)
- no juices, carbonated water or pop/soft-drinks of any kind
- do not over-drink or under-drink

Select the compromise that seems right for you. Excessive beverage intake can dilute digestive juices. However, lack of fluid can reduce the amount of digestive juices generated. The more liquefied the food in your digestive system, the more accessible it is to the digestive enzymes and ultimately, to your body.

Scheduling your meals:

- most nutritional regimens recommend three meals per day (a larger breakfast, a reasonable lunch and a small dinner)
- those with very weak digestive systems (and children or athletes) may have to eat more frequently – four to five small meals per day
- whatever your regimen, ensure that you have distinct meals – no grazing between meals. Your digestion needs to rest at some time
- if you have to skip a meal, make certain it is dinner

HOW AND WHERE TO START

5

For those of us who need a more structured step-by-step approach, the following may be of some help.

❋ STAGE 1: FAMILIARIZATION AND DECISIONS

Take a critical look at your health. How are you managing your role as a parent? Spouse? Employee? Do you have the energy it takes to get through your day? Are you content? Emotionally engaged? Feel that your world is supportive of you? Is there anything you can identify that limits the quality of your life?

☐ In the past months, have you felt so tired or unwell that it affected your job performance and satisfaction, the responsibilities you are willing to assume, and ability to get along with bosses or coworkers?

☐ Have you lowered your aspirations to better align with your confidence levels? Was this decision in response to a reduction in your health and energy levels?

☐ From an exercise perspective, have you reduced the frequency, intensity, duration or form of your involvement?

☐ Have you reduced or even changed your activity level from active participation, (hiking, biking, skiing, exercising, playing sports)? Are you taking a spectator approach?

☐ Have you reduced your involvement in activities you normally participate in with your family and friends?

☐ Has your level of responsiveness to the needs of your children and loved ones decreased?

☐ Are you finding day-to-day tasks more challenging and demanding?

READ THESE CHAPTERS

'Quick Reference Lists' under sections:

1. *Avoid the Following*
2. *Diversify Your Food Choices*
3. *Rotate Your Foods*
4. *Where to Get the Ingredients*

Important: *The cardinal rules of my regimen are individuality and versatility. Do not hesitate to adapt anything I suggest to your individual needs. For example, start by making one proper meal according to my recommendations once a day or once a week. When your body and your lifestyle become accustomed to this improvement, implement other changes. This may take several days to a few weeks. Just keep working on it.*

The duration of each stage is intended to be individualized by the reader. Each stage can mean a week or less to some; months to others.

IDENTIFY THE DEFICIENCIES IN YOUR HEALTH, FUNCTION AND ENERGY

Do you experience any of the following?

- [ ] undesirable weight gain or weight loss
- [ ] poor appetite or a tendency to over-eat
- [ ] digestive problems
- [ ] elimination issues
- [ ] urination issues
- [ ] skin problems
- [ ] irritability
- [ ] distractibility and difficulty concentrating
- [ ] impatience
- [ ] sadness
- [ ] anxiety or distress
- [ ] negativity
- [ ] hypoglycemic reactions (dizziness)
- [ ] low sex drive
- [ ] low self-esteem
- [ ] sleep disturbances, insomnia or hyper-somnia (too much sleep)
- [ ] headaches
- [ ] easily injured
- [ ] susceptibility to colds and flus
- [ ] easily fatigued and general tiredness
- [ ] reduction in strength

- [ ] reduced endurance and stamina
- [ ] feeling stiff or increased muscle tension
- [ ] poor flexibility
- [ ] joint and muscle pain or discomfort
- [ ] general increase in pain or discomfort
- [ ] shortness of breath
- [ ] feeling of accelerated ageing
- [ ] poor healing and recuperation
- [ ] feeling unwell
- [ ] low motivation
- [ ] apathy
- [ ] indecisiveness and avoidance
- [ ] fatigue after meals
- [ ] waking up not refreshed
- [ ] diminished interest in life
- [ ] loss of pleasure
- [ ] inability or little inclination to improve

Note: While this is not intended to be an exhaustive audit, establishing a benchmark for how you feel is the first step to making changes.

MANAGE EACH DEFICIENCY AND IMPROVE THE QUALITY OF YOUR LIFE AND FUTURE

Write down the wishes and dreams you could realize if you were healthy and full of vitality.

For Example, "If I had…"

☐ more energy, I could do…

☐ less pain, I could do…

☐ no symptoms associated with asthma, diarrhea, chronic fatigue, etc. I could do …

TAKE OFF THE ROSE-COLOURED GLASSES AND TRY TO PICTURE WHAT COULD HAPPEN IF YOU MAKE NO CHANGES

☐ accelerated ageing of your physical appearance

☐ further progression of your condition

☐ more than age-related reduction in functional capacities and performance

☐ increased pain

☐ lowered energy and activity levels

☐ decreased capacity to participate in anything requiring a healthy body (biking, hiking, canoeing, skiing, golfing)

☐ surrendering your favourite activities

☐ reduced ability to assist, teach or play with your children

☐ less fun with family and friends

☐ increased social isolation

☐ further weight gain

☐ increased dependency on prescription drugs and mechanical aids

☐ forced retirement

☐ more time in hospital as a patient

☐ reduced capacity for self-care and decision-making

HOW MUCH TIME PER DAY ARE YOU PREPARED TO COMMIT TO YOUR HEALTH?

☐ 5 to 15 minutes

☐ 15 to 30 minutes

☐ 30 to 60 minutes

☐ 60 to 90 minutes

☐ 120 to 180 minutes

☐ more if required. This will be necessary for some medical conditions.

Note: It is important that you meet your time commitment regardless of your daily obstacles.

❊ STAGE 2: CLEAN UP, REPLACE AND EXPERIMENT

CLEAN UP AND REPLACE IN WEEK ONE

- **Discard** old condiments, crackers, wheat products, leftovers, processed, junk and other offending foods
  Replace them with healthier choices
- **Locate** stores that carry natural foods and the foods recommended in the program
- **Start** buying the recommended foods, ingredients (organic or natural if possible) and use them in your cooking. If required, bring this book with you for reference when shopping

EXPERIMENT FOR WEEKS TWO, THREE AND FOUR

- **Make small changes** (chew your food thoroughly, drink warm tea or warm filtered water instead of soft drinks; establish a regular time for your meals)
- **Make healthier choices and meals** based on my recommendations (cooking at home is the best, but if you need to eat out adapt your orders, e.g. replace potatoes with cooked vegetables)
- **Observe and compare** how you feel when eating recommended foods versus those that should be eliminated
  Keep a food diary and note not only what you eat, but also how you feel
- **Make an effort to identify the foods that are aggravating your system and eliminate them**
  - Even if these may be foods listed in my Hot List as recommended foods!
  - Remember, we all are unique and respond differently to different foods!

❊ STAGE 3: VARIETY/DIVERSIFICATION

DIVERSIFY IN WEEKS FIVE AND SIX

- **Introduce** new foods and increase the variety of foods in your diet
- **Do not eat** the same food every day
- **Use ingredients NOT on the Avoid List when making meals.** Try setting goals (e.g. once a day or every second day; breakfasts or dinners for a week, etc.)

IMPROVE

- **Drink warm liquids and consume your meals warm**. If your meals are not warm, at least drink something warm with them
- **Chew your food** 20 or more times
- **Establish a regular time** for your meals
- **Cook enough** for lunch. For example, if you used a slow cooker overnight or cooked in the morning. Invest in a good thermos to keep food warm
- **Drink** a variety of warm teas

RECORD

- **Write down what you eat**
  - whatever goes into your mouth goes on the paper (a few words are enough, e.g. rice, lentils, chicken, vegetables, oregano, thyme)

✳ STAGE 4: ROTATION

ROTATE ON WEEK SEVEN

- **Start rotating your foods.** If you eat one kind of food one day, do not consume it for another four or more consecutive days
  <u>Eat different foods each day for four days or more</u>
- **Do not repeat** the same four-days-worth of recipes and food choices. Each day in the new four-day cycle has to be different from the days in the previous four-day rotation
- **These changes are in addition** to those you have made in the previous stages
- **Cook** as many of the recommended foods as possible
- **Increase frequency** of cooking more of the recommended foods

❋ STAGE 5: EXPAND AND OPTIMIZE

EXPAND AND OPTIMIZE FOR LIFE

- **Establish small realistic objectives and meet them** (e.g. cook or select one or two meals per day based on my recommended approach). Alternatively, you may decide to state your objectives in percentage terms and commit to making 60%, 70% or more of your meals based on my recommendations
- **Read** the rest of the book and keep improving your dietary regimen
- **Continue a daily practice of writing down foods and ingredients you consume**

Note: Results are usually proportional to the changes made. Improvements include feeling lighter, more optimistic, confident, healthier and less tired.

"Make your effort match
 your expectations"

THE REGIMEN

This is what this book is about!

The next pages are the most important part of the book. This is all you need to read if you do not have the energy or time to read anything more. It is the summary of what you need to know to cook your way to heath and vitality.

It contains chapters:

6   **QUICK REFERENCE LIST**

7   **HOT LIST OF RECOMMENDED FOODS**

8   **HEALTHY SUBSTITUTIONS**

9   **ROTATE YOUR FOODS AND KEEP A FOOD DIARY**

10   **MENU SAMPLE**

6

KEY RECOMMENDATIONS:

1. All ingredients must be cooked, including fruits and vegetables

2. All beverages must be consumed warm

3. Do not eat cold foods

4. Serve food promptly after cooking it

5. Do not reheat leftovers – avoid them if at all possible. Their nutritional value is drastically reduced and consuming them may aggravate digestion

6. To avoid wasting food, place cooked or partially cooked food into a preheated thermos while still hot and eat it before it gets cold

7. Chew each mouthful at least 20 times; this helps digestion immensely

AVOID:

Note: Dry powdered red, chili, cayenne, green or other peppers are allowed in small 'seasoning' quantities but only for those who do not react to them adversely.

■ Alcohol
■ Canned food
■ Chocolate
■ Coffee
■ Fast foods
■ Processed foods
■ Junk food
■ Foods with additives
■ Soy and soy products
■ Sugar
■ Peanuts

■ Apples
■ Bananas
■ Citrus fruits
■ Juices: all fruit and vegetable

■ Corn
■ Eggplant
■ Mushrooms
■ Yams
■ All peppers
■ Potatoes
■ Sweet potatoes
■ Tomatoes

■ Wheat and wheat-based grains: kamut, semolina, spelt, couscous, bulgur, triticale

■ Shellfish
■ Milk
■ Yogurt

■ Cheese
■ Buttermilk
■ Cream
■ Goat milk and sheep milk products

■ Large beans: lima and kidney

■ Margarine
■ Trans fats
■ Shortening partially hydrogenated vegetable oils

FRUITS

· should be consumed in small amounts only
· those with chronic illnesses may need to avoid them temporarily
· should be cooked
· preferably replaced by berries (also cooked)
· if using, focus on consuming a variety of fruits
· eat fruit types that you normally do not consume

Most fruits are considered potentially allergenic or irritating to our digestive or other systems. This is the reason why I am not including a list of recommended fruits.

If you can't live without fruit, maintain your food diary noting how you feel after eating fruit. If it aggravates your system, eliminate it from your diet. You may be able to reintroduce it at a later date.

SEASONINGS AND FLAVOURINGS

· rotate herbs and spices to reduce the potential for developing sensitivities
· enjoy the diverse medicinal benefits of many culinary herbs and spices
· herbs and spices also enhance digestion, palatability, aroma and the appearance of food
· cook with organic culinary herbs and spices and make your own condiments using the recipes included in this book

AVOID ALL OTHER FOODS YOU SUSPECT TO BE IRRITATING

Your food diary is key to helping you identify patterns. Start becoming attuned to how you feel and how your body functions. What you eliminate from your diet is highly individual and might include the foods we would normally consider less allergenic such as fish, eggs, pork, other meats, garlic, onions, carrots, cabbage, cauliflower, some nuts and flax seeds. When reintroducing a food you suspect is irritating your system, try cooking and eating it in small quantities. Listen to your body.

When possible, choose certified organic sources, non-GMO, free range, etc. This is especially important for animal products.

READING LABELS: IF IT SOUNDS LIKE A CHEMICAL, IT PROBABLY IS.

Beware of the term 'natural'. Its definition within Canadian manufacturing practices is so broad-based, it can include substances as harmful as MSG.

DIVERSIFY YOUR FOOD CHOICES

Do not consume the same food every day – keep variety in your diet.
All too often we get into a food rut and simply need a reminder of all the different foods out there. Focus on introducing a variety of foods. The goal is to **create simple, fresh, tasty meals from basic ingredients. Each meal should include protein and vegetables. A more complete meal may also include grains and beans.**

- Proteins I recommend include meat, fish, poultry, eggs, beans, nuts and seeds. No dairy. Nuts, seeds and beans can be used in addition to other proteins, providing you do not react to them. (No dairy protein).

ROTATE YOUR FOODS

Make certain to eat different foods each day for four or more days. This means that if you eat a specific food on Monday, the earliest time you can eat it again is Friday.

KEEP A FOOD DIARY

Please do not neglect this step. It's critical to keep a written record of what you eat and drink along with how your body responds.

HOT LIST OF RECOMMENDED FOODS

HOT LIST: ANIMAL PROTEINS

- beef
- bison
- exotic meats
- fish (wild, cold water, not canned): haddock, halibut, herring, mackerel, salmon, trout, sardines, tuna
- lamb, mutton, llama
- poultry (chicken, turkey, geese, ducks)
- game birds (pheasant, partridge, geese, ducks, grouse)
- ostrich
- pork (only verifiably free-range organic or wild boar)
- rabbit
- venison

ORGAN MEATS
If you are not averse to eating internal organs, include them also, but they must be certified organic or from healthy wild animals. Organ meats have higher nutritional value than muscle meat.

FISH SENSE
Select smaller-sized fish. These had less time to accumulate toxic substances from their habitat. Many people are allergic to the fish itself or mercury and/or other pollutants in the fish.

HOT LIST: BEANS/LENTILS

- adzuki
- bean sprouts
- black beans
- black-eyed beans
- black turtle beans
- chickpeas
- dhal (any small dhal)
- green beans
- great northern beans
- lentils: French, brown, red/pink, yellow
- mung beans
- navy beans
- peas: green, yellow, split
- pinto beans
- romano beans

EXCLUDE KIDNEY, LIMA AND OTHER LARGE BEANS
If you can tolerate beans, include them. Cooked fresh beans, fresh green peas and sprouted beans are easier on our systems than their dried counterparts. Smaller beans are better.

See the Beans Crash Course for advice on how to cook beans to improve digestion.

HOT LIST: GRAINS

- amaranth
- barley
- brown rice, wild rice
- buckwheat
- millet
- oats
- quinoa
- rye
- sorghum
- tapioca
- teff

HOT LIST: VEGETABLES

VEGETABLES

- *use all colours and varieties of vegetables – the more vibrant the better*
- *rotate them as much as possible*
- *consume at least three to four kinds of vegetables of a different colour every day*
- *make an effort to buy different vegetables on each shopping trip*

- alfalfa sprouts
- bamboo shoots
- artichoke
- asparagus
- bean sprouts
- beet tops and beet roots
- black Spanish radish
- bok choy
- broccoli
- Brussels sprouts
- burdock leaves and roots
- cabbage: green, red/purple, savoy
- cauliflower
- carrots
- celery
- chard
- chives
- collard
- cucumbers
- daikon: greens and roots
- dandelion leaves, flowers, roots
- endive
- escarole

- Jerusalem artichoke
- kale
- kohlrabi
- leeks
- romaine lettuce
- mustard greens
- parsley
- parsnip
- peas: green, snow
- pumpkin
- radish
- rapini
- rutabaga
- scallions
- spinach
- squash: acorn, buttercup, butternut, hubbard, summer
- string beans
- swiss chard
- turnip
- water chestnut
- watercress
- zucchini
- wild herbs

 HOT LIST: SEA VEGETABLES

PAY ATTENTION

Please eat only those nuts and seeds you tolerate well. If in doubt, avoid them, even if it means all of them! Grind or soak hard seeds. Roasting also improves their digestibility.

- kelp
- dulse
- nori
- kombu

- hijiki
- Irish moss
- arame

HOT LIST: SEEDS AND NUTS (AND THEIR BUTTERS)

- almonds
- Brazil nuts
- cashews
- coconut
- hazelnuts
- macadamia nuts
- pecans

- pine nuts
- walnuts
- flax
- hemp
- pumpkin
- poppy
- sesame: black or brown
- sunflower

HOT LIST: OILS AND FATS

- fish oil
- flax seed oil (do not heat)
- canola
- butter
- coconut oil (thick like butter and as digestible as dairy butter because it contains

- medium chain fatty acids that are easier to digest)
- cooked bone marrow (highly recommended if you are able to cook quality bones)
- olive oil
- pumpkin seed butter

Note:

OILS

■ *Please use virgin oils or first cold pressed oils only. Non-GMO certified organic is ideal. Verify that the producer tests the seeds for GMO. Do not heat to high temperatures.*

■ *Avoid oils extracted with solvents because they may contain toxic residues. Also avoid oils extracted with high heat. Look for oils that state 'cold pressed' on the label.*

■ *Do not use oils for stir-frying or frying. See the Stir-Frying Crash Course for more information. Use organic butter and organic clarified butter. Heavy rice oil used in Chinese Stir-frying has a higher burning point but Chinese regulations concerning food safety and toxic content do not measure up to ours.*

■ *Butter is the only dairy product I recommend because it contains limited quantities of irritating protein. Clarified butter is even better for those who are very sensitive.*

HOT LIST: SWEET AND SUGAR REPLACEMENTS

- rice syrup and barley malt
- licorice and stevia
- dry fruits
- fresh ripe cooked fruits
- maple syrup
- beet syrup
- agave syrup

- fructose
- yacon syrup
- sorghum syrup or pure sorghum (sorghum molasses contains sugar molasses)
- beet syrup
- sucanat

HOT LIST: BEVERAGES

- purified water
- coffee substitutes, e.g. bamboo, chicory (check the labels for allergens)

- herbal teas: loose leaf teas taste better and are healthier
- mineral water (verify the content and source)

HOT LIST: FERMENTED SOY PRODUCTS

- miso
- natto
- tempeh

 ## HOT LIST: FRUITS

- cooked fruit in moderation, preferably replaced by berries

 ## HOT LIST: BERRIES

- blackberry
- marionberry
- boysenberry
- blueberry
- cranberry
- currants
- goji berry
- gooseberry
- elderberry

- juneberry
- serviceberry
- huckleberry
- lingonberry
- raspberry
- salmonberry
- saskatoon berry
- strawberry (caution potential sensitivities)

Note: Miso is also made from barley, rice or rye.

Caution: Many soy products contain allergenic and other additives.

- *fermented soy can be consumed only one out of four or more days, provided you have not been eating soy products often and do not react to them adversely*

BERRIES
- *should be consumed in small amounts only*
- *should be cooked*
- *eat berry types that you normally do not consume*
- *focus on eating a wider variety of berries*

HEALTHY SUBSTITUTIONS

Here's a start-up reference list to help you make the transition to allergy-free, healthy eating. Pay attention to the foods you eat and identify those that are aggravating. Try the following replacements:

AGGRAVATING FOODS	HEALTHY REPLACEMENTS
Cheese	Almond cheese (if you can tolerate it). Caution.
Chocolate	Carob (dark roasted powder is tastier)
Coffee	Caf-lib™, Teecchino™, Cafix™, Caffree™, Inka™, Raja's Cup™, Roma™, Roastaroma™. Herbal teas: bamboo, chicory, dandelion.
Corn	Millet, rice, quinoa, amaranth, barley, buckwheat, oat, rye, teff
Eggs	Can be consumed if you are not allergic to them. Refer to the condiments section to make an egg substitute. Less sensitive individuals might substitute duck or other fowl eggs for chicken eggs.
Garlic	Use the real thing unless you are sensitive to it, substitute usnea if you must. Refer to the section *Medicinal Herbs in the Kitchen*. Usnea must be boiled.
Gluten	If you're sensitive, avoid wheat, barley, oats, rye, triticale, kamut and millet and buckwheat. Try rice, teff, amaranth, quinoa, tapioca, cassava and arrowroot flours.
Kidney beans	Adzuki beans
Lactose	'Pareve'-marked foods (milk-free, no lactose). Note: lactate, lactic acid and lact-albumin don't contain lactose.
Lime/Lemon juice	In general, heated lime and lemon juice become less irritating. Vinegar (not malt vinegar for those who have barley allergies).
Milk	Milk made from nuts such as almond, cashews, brazil nuts, hazelnut, coconut, or from seeds such as sesame, sunflower or grains like rice, quinoa and oat.

AGGRAVATING FOODS	HEALTHY REPLACEMENTS
Mushrooms	Usnea, also known and marketed as Usno, Binan or Sun–lo; please see the *Crash Course in Seasoning Combinations and Recommended Use* for more information
Peanut butter	Bean spreads, nut butters you can tolerate, egg spreads; note that 'Pea-butter', a commercial substitute made from chickpeas, contains sugar
Potatoes	Jerusalem artichokes (great in soups), creamy-mashed cauliflower; for a more robust flavour, try rutabaga, radish, kohlrabi and squash
Table salt	Pure coarse salt, kosher salt, pickling salt, sea salt
Soy/Tofu	Rice milk, nut milks (almond, cashew), sesame seed milk, nut cheeses and animal protein. Note: lecithin is from soy.
Soybean	Other small beans, legumes and lentils
Starch (corn or potato)	Tapioca starch
Sugar	Rice syrup, buckwheat syrup, barley malt, stevia, licorice, sorghum molasses, date sugar, berry sugar – for recipes requiring powdered sweetener
Wheat	Buckwheat, rye, oat, rice, millet, quinoa, barley, amaranth, teff and sorghum
Wraps	Hypoallergenic pancakes, crackers, breads and cooked wraps (without additives)

HEALTHY SUBSTITUTES FOR: WHEAT, BAKING POWDER, THICKENERS, SWEETS, BAD FATS, SOY AND EGGS

■ WHEAT-FREE FLOUR SUBSTITUTIONS

Grind and use any of the following:
Buckwheat, rye, oat, rice, millet, quinoa, barley, amaranth, sorghum and teff. Or, make your own wheat-free baking flour:

3 c. white rice flour
3 c. brown rice flour
1 c. tapioca flour
1 c. xanthan gum

* double the recipe as required
* combine all ingredients
* store in an airtight container in the freezer compartment

* soaking improves digestibility and improves the texture (important for pancakes, crackers)
* when using in a recipe, bake at 10° to 20° F lower than the recipe recommends for wheat
* increase the baking time accordingly (test with a toothpick)
* use a small amount of oil to make a stronger crust

■ DO NOT EXPECT NON-WHEAT FLOUR TO RISE AS MUCH AS WHEAT FLOUR

Compensate by:

* keeping batter thin, ideally around 6 cm or less
* increasing the baking powder amount by ½ t. per c. (use our recipe and keep in mind that adding more baking powder is not ideal)
* avoiding the use of baking powder altogether and use more flat breads, pancakes...
* adding ground seeds (flax seeds) to thicken and improve the texture (will not help the dough to rise)
* adding the following amount of xanthan or guar gum to one cup of non-wheat flour to impove binding:
  * 1 to 2 t. for breads or pizza
  * ½ to 1 t. for cakes
  * 0 to 1½ t. for cookies
  * 2 T. green peas or bean flour per 1 c. non-wheat flour

IMPORTANT
Xanthan gum, also referred to as Zanthan gum, is used to improve the binding capacity of gluten-free flour or other non-wheat flours.

The gluten in wheat provides the special binding capacity that is not present in non-wheat flours. There is a concern that some people may react to the xanthan or guar gum. The argument is based on the fact that corn is used as a substrate in the production of xanthan gum and guar gum is made from a plant that belongs to the legume family.

If you react to any of these, you may experiment with pre-gel starch, pectin, gelatin and their combinations.

■ BAKING POWDER SUBSTITUTE

Avoid the wheat and corn in commercial products and make your own baking powder for less.

2 t. cream of tartar
1 t. baking soda
1 t. salt (optional)

- Drop into a small covered container and shake well to blend
- Makes 4 teaspoons
- Guidelines for use are 1 t. per cup of flour
- Store in an airtight container
- Mix before using

■ HEALTHY THICKENER SUBSTITUTES

Ground sesame seeds, hemp seeds or other seeds and nuts are ideal thickeners. So too barley, buckwheat or other less-allergenic grain flour and tapioca flour.

- If you prefer a thickener which doesn't add much taste to the recipe, use barley or buckwheat flour
- Use comparatively less arrowroot or sorghum powder than any other flour; a little goes a long way
- Tapioca starch must be dissolved in cold water before adding it to hot mixtures

■ SWEETENER SUBSTITUTES

Brown rice, buckwheat and barley malt syrup are made from complex carbohydrates. They are healthier alternatives to simple sugars because they do not disturb the blood glucose balance the way sugar does. They are also less sweet than sugar. Berry and date sugar are not the best, but are still better than sugar.

Regardless of preference, do not overuse any sweeteners. They are non-essential and non-productive to building better health. As your condition and nutrition improves, you will notice that your craving for sweets will subside or disappear altogether.

Browse the many natural replacements found at your local health food stores, and try these:

Rice or buckwheat syrup and barley malt
- less sweet than sugar but satisfying – made from complex carbohydrates
- always check the labels for allergens

Note: Commercially produced baking powder often contains wheat flour, corn, aluminum and other undesirable additives. Buy organic or make your own as needed.

Hint: Make up small batches of baking powder. The ingredients are acid and alkaline and will neutralize each other when stored.

Hint: Increase the amount of protein in your diet to reduce cravings for sweets.

Dry fruits or berries
- soak in water and blend to replicate syrup texture (bahari or other dates, figs, prunes)
- try using in place of sugar in recipes for a unique taste
- when serving as a topping, simmer them for a few minutes to destroy potential mould residue

Fresh ripe fruits or berries
- bake or stir-fry with cloves, cinnamon and black pepper

Licorice and stevia (sweet herbs)
- licorice is 50 times sweeter than sugar
- stevia is 150 times sweeter than sugar
- white or liquid stevia are processed, so avoid them if possible

Maple, berry and date sugar
- use for special occasions or for baking that requires a dry sweetener

The following are concentrated sweeteners. Treat them as a slightly better sugar.

Honey
- **NO unpasteurized honey** for children under one year
- twice as sweet as sugar, so measure accordingly if you choose to use it

Maple syrup
- treat it as a tasty, more expensive sugar; as an added bonus, maple syrup contains minerals and vitamins

Yacon Syrup
- made from the root of the South American yacon plant, processed at 140° C

Sorghum syrup or pure sorghum (sorghum molasses contains sugarcane molasses)
- made from sorghum cane

Beet syrup
- is a less refined and less concentrated form of sugar
- taste is usually considered inferior to sugar

Sucanat
- made by the evaporation of sugar cane juice at a temperature higher than 100°C

Agave syrup
- made from a cactus-like plant – 25% sweeter than sugar

Fructose
- acknowledged to have adverse effects on our health
- less demanding on insulin release than regular sugar

DO NOT USE ARTIFICIAL SWEETENERS OF ANY KIND.

Note: Do not consume sweetener alone. Always eat something else with it (non-wheat pancakes, porridge, wheat-free bread, etc.).

■ CHOCOLATE

If chocolate is an absolute must for you, try eating dark chocolate instead. Ideally, the dark chocolate should be bitter and made without sugar and milk, two ingredients to avoid. Most people do not realise that chocolate is crude opium.

■ GOOD FATS

Recommended oils are extra virgin olive oil, flax seed oil, unrefined coconut oil and butter.

Use extra virgin, virgin or first cold-pressed oils that are sold in opaque glass containers. Light, air, high temperature and pressure as well as chemical solvents destroy the nutritional qualities of oil. In addition, solvents leave harmful residues. The green color in extra-virgin olive oil is not produced by harmful residues but by a presence of plant-based particles or molecules beneficial to our health.

Keep your oils tightly closed in dark glass containers and store in a dark, cool place. Refrigeration is recommended by some oil manufacturers. The clouding from refrigeration won't harm the oil.

Clarified Butter (aka Ghee)

Many who can't tolerate butter can use clarified butter. It adds great flavour and, when softened, can replace oil or used halved with oil. Clarified butter will take more heat without burning.

1 lb. butter

- Heat the butter in a heavy saucepan over very low heat for 1 hour
- Butter will separate into three layers: milk solids (white foam on top), clarified butter in the middle, and the whey and milk solids at the bottom of the pan
- Carefully skim off all foam, then pour off the yellow liquid (the middle layer) into a container for storage. Ensure you do not pour any of the solids from the bottom layer!
- Store in an airtight container in the refrigerator

Note: All oils are not created equal. Organic flax seed oil from one grower and processing manufacturer may be far superior to another flax seed oil grown organically and processed somewhere else. Choose oils that have little or no genetically modified seed content, good taste and do not use chemicals, high heat or excessive pressures in the extraction process.

SEA VEGETABLES AND FERMENTED SOY PRODUCTS

■ SEA VEGETABLES

The least healthy patients genuinely benefit from the addition of sea vegetables to their diet. Use them similarly to how you use dried herbs. Sea vegetables include: kelp, dulse, nori, kombu, hijiki, Irish moss and arame. These are high in iodine and other micronutrients which are harder to obtain from land-dwelling food sources. Sea vegetables are usually available at health food or Asian stores.

Sea vegetables provide a unique and pleasant flavour to food when used in the right quantity and when combined with seasonings. In addition, sea vegetables reduce the need for salt. As with any other food beware of sensitivities or allergies.

■ FERMENTED SOY PRODUCTS

It is now evident that the health benefits attributed to non-fermented soy products have been highly distorted. In fact, these products can have harmful effects on our health. Non-fermented soy does not have the benefits inherent to the fermentation process. There are many fermented soy products on the market, some of the more common ones are miso, natto and tempeh which are often sold in specialty aisles in your corner grocery store.

I would like to stress that many of these fermented products contain allergenic foods that are added in the manufacturing process. In addition, some of the ingredients come from countries where food safety is not perceived as an important factor. Consumers should exercise caution even if these products were produced in North America because U.S. and Canadian manufacturers are not obliged to disclose ingredients added in the manufacturing process.

The positive aspect is that some manufacturers are starting to reduce or replace the soy when producing some of these fermented products. For example, other grains and beans such as barley, rice, buckwheat, quinoa, millet, adzuki and black beans are used.

EGG SUBSTITUTES

If you are allergic to eggs, consider one of these for your recipes:

Option 1:
- 3 T. arrowroot powder
- 1 t. guar gum or xanthan gum
- 3 T. water

Option 2:
- 1 T. ground flax or psyllium seeds
- 3 T. water or other liquid

Option 3:
- 1½ T. ground sesame seeds or hemp seeds
- 3 T. water or other liquid

■ Mix well. Each of the above options replaces one egg.

ROTATE YOUR FOODS AND KEEP A FOOD DIARY

Make certain to eat something different every day for four or more days. This means that you are allowed to eat the same food only one day within a four-day period.

REMINDER: CANNED AND PROCESSED FOODS MUST BE AVOIDED.

This eating regimen ensures more nutritious variety in your diet, while improving your digestion, and your tolerance of different foods. The program is based on rotating grains, beans, meats, nuts, seeds and, to some extent, vegetables.

FOUR-DAY ROTATION EXAMPLE

Using two different meals per day (e.g. same food for breakfast and lunch).

Note: You may replace grains with cooked vegetables.

Proteins						
Mon	Tue	Wed	Thu	Fri	Sat	Sun
eggs	beef	chicken	cashew nuts	turkey	eggs	sesame seeds
turkey	herring	lamb	venison	halibut	buffalo	lamb

Note: Blood type O may need to reduce the amount of beans they consume. They do better with meat and vegetables.

Grains						
Mon	Tue	Wed	Thu	Fri	Sat	Sun
oats	barley	millet	teff	rice	oats	buckwheat
rice	quinoa	buckwheat	rye	amaranth	millet	barley

Beans						
Mon	Tue	Wed	Thu	Fri	Sat	Sun
lentils	black beans	chickpeas	black-eyed peas	green beans	dhal (lentils)	adzuki beans

Note: A small amount of nuts and seeds can be used to replace meat, if not aggravating.

Nuts or Seeds (if tolerated, otherwise exclude them)						
Mon	Tue	Wed	Thu	Fri	Sat	Sun
walnuts	sesame seeds	flax seeds	hazelnuts	hemp seed	pumpkin seeds	brazilian nuts

Don't use the same rotation menu each week. For example, you shouldn't always be eating beef with barley. If you do, you could become sensitive to this specific combination of foods. As shown in the above example menu tables, there are more than enough combinations possible to avoid this problem.

KEY POINTS OF THE ROTATION DIET

- *Remember to also rotate toppings, condiments, culinary herbs and spices*

- *Do not use the same nuts or seeds more than one day within a four-day period. For example, alternate among sesame seeds, cashews, pumpkin seeds, walnuts and hemp seeds; this applies to milk and butters made from them*

- *Do not use the same beans more than one day within a four-day period; for example, alternate among black beans, chickpeas, adzuki beans, pinto beans, lentils, green peas and black eyed peas*

- *Do not use beans or nuts or seeds if you find them irritating. Replace them with substitutes like meat, eggs, butter, avocado, beans...*

- *In most cases, cooked vegetables, and to some extent cooked fresh beans, do not have to be diligently rotated. In other words, you may consume the same vegetables and fresh beans for more than one day in a four-day rotation; however, make certain that you do not use them as often in the following four-day rotation*

- *Lunches are easy if you invest in a wide-mouth thermos for solid foods and a regular, glass-lined thermos for beverages*

- *If you can't handle a specific grain, replace it with another grain or with a vegetable*

- *Meat, fish and poultry have not been included in the breakfast menu because most people in our culture find it unappealing. Ideally, breakfast should be the main meal of the day; try to have a different protein (meat, fish or poultry) for each of your breakfast, lunch and dinner meals. Otherwise use nuts, seeds, beans and eggs for proteins.*

KEEP A RECORD OF WHAT YOU EAT AND HOW YOUR BODY RESPONDS TO IT.

KEEP A FOOD DIARY

It is absolutely critical to keep a written record of what you eat and drink, and how your body reacts to it. Everything that goes into your mouth has to be written down. Make certain to record the foods you suspect aggravate you. Usually patients have a rapid, adverse reaction that occurs within minutes or hours after eating a particular food. However, a delayed reaction can take place the next day or even later, making it harder to identify the offending food.

Your food diary is essential for planning your meals and diversifying your diet for optimum health and vitality. Above all, it helps you identify aggravating foods which should then be eliminated from your diet until you desensitize your system to them.

Note: *Highly sensitive people may only be able to tolerate the same food once in seven days. Furthermore, they might only be able to eat the same food once per day. Obviously, these individuals will have to be very creative when designing their own programs.*

DAY	MENU
1	**BREAKFAST AND LUNCH** Parsnip and Carrot Pancakes (use oat flour) with nut seed butter or warm alternative milk or warm tea **DINNER** Un-tomato Red Sauce or Chili over rice or non-wheat pasta (rice pasta) with lamb or game meat (can be added when making the chili/sauce). *Vegetarian option:* replace meat with your preferred bean
2	**BREAKFAST AND LUNCH** Hot Quinoa or Savory Quinoa with sautéed fresh string beans and eggs **DINNER** Roasted Poultry (turkey, duck) *Vegetarian option:* Chickpea Vegetable Soup with Rye Bread
3	**BREAKFAST AND LUNCH** Buckwheat Barley Pancakes/Wrap filled with stir-fried fresh green or other beans, vegetables, nuts/seeds or beef/bison, game meat *The dough for the wrap can be made ahead of time* **DINNER** Curried Meat with Vegetables *Vegetarian option:* Velvety Butternut Squash Soup with Millet Bread
4	**BREAKFAST AND LUNCH** Amaranth Pancakes or Basic Amaranth (porridge) with bean spread or nut/seed butter, warm alternative milk or warm tea **DINNER** Steamed Salmon with Greens and String Beans *Vegetarian option:* Stir-Fried Vegetables with String Beans and Teff Cooked Simply

DAY	MENU
5	**BREAKFAST AND LUNCH** Sorghum Porridge or Tortilla from rice with a choice of spread made from avocado, eggs, beans, nuts or seeds **DINNER** Poultry (chicken, goose…) with Coconut Rice and stir-fried or steamed vegetables *Vegetarian option:* Overnight Lentil soup with French Baguette (may be baked ahead of time) and Avocado Egg Spread
6	**BREAKFAST AND LUNCH** Oatmeal Porridge or Oatmeal Pancakes with Wilted Salad and ground nuts/seeds or Veggie Delight **DINNER** Garlic Fried Lamb or Lamb stir-fried in coriander and cumin with stir-fried or steamed vegetables of your choice *Vegetarian option:* Green Beans, Chestnut, Asparagus Salad with Savory Quinoa and Chopped Coconut.
7	**BREAKFAST AND LUNCH** Gingerbread Cake with a choice of a spread or Quick Buckwheat Porridge with eggs and vegetables **DINNER** Baked Trout (or other wild cold water fish) with choice of vegetables *Vegetarian option:* Black Bean Egg Soup with Rye Bread (Light or Sour Dough)
8	**BREAKFAST AND LUNCH** Amaranth Muffins or Pancakes or Basic Amaranth (porridge) with bean spread or nut/seed butter, warm alternative milk or warm tea **DINNER** Beef Goulash with steamed vegetables of your choice and beans *Vegetarian option:* Millet Crackers, steamed vegetable with avocado and bean spread or dip
DAY	MENU
9	**BREAKFAST AND LUNCH** Three-Minute Bean Sprout Soup with tortillas or crackers made from barley or rice and organic coconut or dairy butter **DINNER** Meat or Veggie Rice Pancakes (use turkey or other fowl)

10	BREAKFAST AND LUNCH Parsnip/Carrot Pancakes (use oat flour) or Oat Porridge with nut/seed butter or warm alternative milk or warm tea DINNER Green Pea Vegetable Soup (or Purée) or Lentil Vegetable Soup (or Purée). Optional: add meat in the last few minutes of cooking or use stir-fried lamb or exotic meat (venison, ostrich, llama, goose, chevron, rabbit, duck, partridge or heart of any meat)
11	BREAKFAST AND LUNCH Buckwheat Flour Pancakes with nut/seed butter or warm alternative milk or warm tea. Optional: cooked fruits such as steamed peaches or stir-fried strawberries, blackberries, blueberries, raspberries or saskatoon berries Remember: The nut or seed butter and fruit or berries can be used once only over four days. DINNER Fish of your choice (Halibut, Trout ...) with vegetables *Vegetarian option:* Cream of Broccoli and Cauliflower Soup with One-Pan Teff Bread or Teff Pancakes
12	BREAKFAST AND LUNCH Quick Roasted Porridge from Rye Grain with vegetables and seeds or eggs DINNER One-dish Millet and Lentils with stir-fried vegetables and beef/buffalo or their heart meat *Vegetarian option:* same recipe but skip the meat

Substitute the following for either day's menu at your discretion or incorporate into your rotation for variety.

DAY	MENU
13	BREAKFAST AND LUNCH Sorghum Porridge or Tortilla from barley or rice with a choice of spread made from avocado, beans, nuts, seeds or Born Again Turkey Sandwich Filling DINNER Poultry with Asparagus, squash and fresh green peas (chicken will do but other fowl is preferred) *Vegetarian option:* skip the meat and replace with nuts/seeds
14	BREAKFAST AND LUNCH Amaranth Pancakes with bean spread or nut/seed butter or Basic Amaranth (porridge) cooked with chopped vegetables, bean sprouts and warm alternative milk or warm tea DINNER Game Meat or Lamb with vegetables and Quick Roasted Porridge (use oat) *Vegetarian option:* Oat Crackers, Hummus and Avocado (Egg) Spread

TIPS FOR CELIAC PATIENTS

11

This book is not written exclusively for celiac patients. However, the recommendations expressed here should become an integral part of any celiac diet. This is with the provision that **celiac patients eliminate gluten-containing or gliadin-mimicking foods. Celiac patients need to take the initiative to identify recipes with these ingredients and make the appropriate substitutions.**

Foods with a high content of gluten are wheat, kamut, triticale, rye, barley, oat and their derivatives. In more severe cases, patients also have to eliminate buckwheat and millet since these contain protein-mimicking alpha-gliadin (a derivative of gluten).

In my opinion, celiac patients would be wise not to limit themselves to the celiac diet alone, regardless of whether they have a provisional or confirmed diagnosis. Typically, these patients have a predisposition to food intolerances and sensitivities. In fact, most patients who come to see me with a previous diagnosis of celiac disease, had more problems with food intolerances and sensitivities than they had with gluten and gliadin.

The majority of recommended celiac diets disregard the autoimmune component of this disease. In essence, they have two major flaws both of which have the potential to aggravate the autoimmune response. First, they recommend consumption of allergenic and aggravating foods. Second, they do not adequately compensate nutritionally for elimination of gluten/gladian-rich foods. If you recall, reducing the variety of foods increases the potential for food sensitivities, intolerances, allergies and autoimmune disorders.

If you already are on the celiac diet, use my program to compensate for the dietary limitations imposed by the elimination of foods containing gluten. Fundamental to my program is the use of the freshest, purest ingredients and the avoidance of processed foods which often contain gluten-rich elements.

Please pay special attention to recommendations I make that are typically omitted from orthodox celiac diets. Revisit the chapter on elimination, substitution, diversification, blood type and rotation. Do not forget to <u>keep a food diary</u> to help you identify foods that aggravate you.

Although the recipes are not exclusively designed for those with confirmed celiac diagnosis, I was sensitive to this condition when writing this book. Many of the recipes are formulated to allow for easy gluten/gliadin elimination, food diversification and ingredient substitution.

If your diagnosis is not certain, start with the general program and your diet diary will help you to detect foods that make you feel uncomfortable. Bloating, gas, pain and nausea are all indications of a food irritation. Just eliminate the offending food, regardless of whether it is gluten-rich or not. Alternatively, you may eliminate known gluten foods at the very start of the program and experiment with reintroducing them after your health has improved.

WHAT I OBSERVED WHEN TREATING PATIENTS WHO HAD BEEN PREVIOUSLY DIAGNOSED WITH CELIAC DISEASE...

- Most new patients claiming a diagnosis of celiac disease did not have adequate diagnostic work done to support such a diagnosis.

- In many cases, their condition could be better explained by a different diagnosis.

- Only a relative minority of these patients achieved a long term improvement on a Celiac diet alone.

- Some reported getting worse early after implementing a prescribed Celiac diet. Others developed an adverse reaction to some of the foods recommended in the Celiac diet when following it on a longer term basis.

- Those who incorporated my hypoaller-genic, rotational, diversified and blood-type specific nutritional regimen into their Celiac diet, have improved. I have to stress that <u>those with accurate diagnoses of Celiac disease needed to eliminate foods containing gluten/gliadin</u>. However, many so-called celiac patients didn't need to eliminate food with high-gluten content to improve, indicating that their diagnoses may have been incorrect.

- An incorrect diagnosis of celiac disease and subsequent elimination of gluten/gliadin foods, makes the recovery even more difficult for many sensitive patients who need a wide variety of foods to achieve optimal health.

" There are few things as important to me as preserving the well-being of my family and Dr. Kodet has helped me in this endeavour more than anyone else. Over the years, day or night, he has always been there to treat any of our health complaints – from childhood illnesses to severe burns and chronic conditions. He helped us overcome some of the most trying events in our lives. I have never left his office feeling anything but sure that his treatments will dramatically help me and my family members heal. "

– Wednesday Shomody, COO, Grantech Engineering International

COOKING ESSENTIALS

12

HEALTHY COOKWARE

■ STAINLESS STEEL

For optimum health, it is best to choose non-porous cookware, ideally surgical stainless steel. Look for cookware or bakeware with the lowest ratio of nickel. Try this test: if your cookware or bakeware has a preferred, lower ratio of nickel, it will attract a magnet. Most connoisseurs would call this stainless inferior, but their criteria is different from ours.

■ GLASS

Glass is always a good choice.

■ ALUMINUM

Avoid aluminum altogether. When heated, the pores of aluminum open, acting as receptacles for tiny food particles. As the pot cools down, the pores close over, trapping particles until the pot is heated again. Next time it's used, the pores reopen and release the old food particles. Not exactly appetizing.

There is continuing debate concerning the role of aluminum in contributing to Alzheimer's disease. The safest approach is to avoid aluminum cookware, eating utensils and aluminum foil. **Interestingly, outside of cookware, anti-perspirants account for our highest exposure to aluminum.**

■ CAST IRON

Although it's generally healthier to broil or bake, some food still requires a frying pan. My favourite remains the classic cast iron. It has to be well-seasoned before use, though some higher-end pans are sold pre-seasoned and are labeled as such.

Contrary to popular belief, cast iron isn't indestructible. In fact, it is a brittle metal which can shatter similarly to glass if dropped.

■ BAKEWARE

Bakeware has improved. Thankfully, steel bakeware is becoming more widely available at a reasonable price.

TIPS ON HOW TO SEASON OR RESEASON YOUR PAN WITHOUT PRODUCING TOXIC BY-PRODUCTS:

- *coat the pan with a <u>thin</u> layer of oil*
- *heat on stovetop at low heat for six to eight hours*
- ***do not allow the heat to reach the smoking point. If heated high enough, any oil will burn and produce carcinogenic compounds***

ABOUT NON-STICK PRODUCTS:

If you are baking gluten-free, avoid non-stick pans, as the bread often comes out raw in the middle. Non-stick cookware is convenient, but I recommend avoiding all non-stick surface coatings.

Glass Pans: **Dark coloured glass absorbs heat better** than clear because it's not as reflective. Glass bakeware is still a fine choice, just remember to **lower the baking temperature by approximately 25° F** to avoid scorching.

APPLIANCES

■ MICROWAVES

Avoid this appliance whenever possible. Instead of engaging in the cancer debate or how food is altered through microwave cooking, try this experiment: microwave a small cup of filtered water and let it cool to room temperature. Place the same amount of non-microwaved filtered water in another cup and place a seed in each. Within the germination period, the seed in the filtered water will sprout and the one in the microwaved water will not. It's easy to find research articles concluding that microwave cooking destroys more nutrients than other forms of traditional cooking.

■ STOVE

Gas stoves are superior for their instant heat. In order to achieve similar benefits when using electric stoves, let the burner heat up before setting on food-filled cookware. Popular opinion states that bringing food to the desired cooking temperature gradually alters its chemical composition and reduces its nutritive value. Proponents of this approach often claim the food is oxidized less when plunged into boiling water because some of the oxygen within the water escapes during boiling. So, boil the water first, then add the food. When steaming, ensure the water is boiling before placing the food in the steam basket.

UTENSILS

Many people favour the use of natural products whenever possible. These are the people who swear by wooden spoons and wooden cutting boards and are against synthetics. My only concern is the porosity of wood and the resulting difficulties in sanitizing it. This is a very real danger when working with eggs, meat and poultry. Many cases of salmonella have occurred due to the contamination of work surfaces, or cross-contamination caused by failing to use separate cutting boards for produce and meat.

Glass and polished stone surfaces tend to quickly dull knife blades and are not suitable for cutting with a cleaver. In addition, both surfaces are too slippery for safe cutting.

Despite the downside, my first choice is still wood, provided it is scalded with boiling water and dried after each use. A possible compromise is to choose a cutting board of guaranteed food-grade plastic from a trusted manufacturer. If anyone in your family is highly sensitive to out-gassing plastics, unwrap the item and let it air outside for a few days or longer before bringing it into the house.

Cooking utensils such as slotted spoons, spatulas and ladles are best in stainless steel. They're durable and easily sanitized.

If you must use rubber scrapers or spatulas, switch to silicone. They withstand higher heat and heavier use than rubber. Also, they do not erode and crumble into food as rubber tends to do when it gets old. That said, some silicone leaching is inevitable.

Here again, use wooden utensils instead of silicone or rubber-based products. Wood is more benign to our body than silicone.

CLEANING COOKING ITEMS

Wash new items before using. Surprisingly, many people use both kitchen items and fabrics right from the store. New does not equal clean and non-toxic.

If you cannot efficiently scrub out something, a kettle for example, fill it to the brim with water and boil for 10 minutes and scrub again.

All the tools of our culinary trade are relatively easy to clean. Wash up with baking soda and a scouring pad or use the mild natural acid of vinegar. Stay away from nasty chemical cleansers. You can visit my website at **www.drkodet.com** under Health Tips for some great natural cleanser ideas.

COUNTERTOPS AND CUTTING BOARDS:

- *wash with hot water, followed by vinegar or baking soda if required*

- *rinse them well with clean water to wash off any cleaning residue (important)*

- *dry well and store cutting boards in an open, well-ventilated place*

- *dedicate one cutting board for meat, fish and poultry, and a second for other foods (some people are even more specific with their cutting boards)*

SAFE FOOD HANDLING

13

There is overwhelming evidence that we should not overdo cleanliness and efforts to sanitize our surroundings. Our immune system has to adapt, strengthen and learn to fight potential invaders. Briefly stated, we need to improve our general resistance to the myriad contaminants around us.

This is neither a new nor an isolated opinion. In fact, even today's naturopathic physicians are trained to think more like **Louis Pasteur, who pronounced, "La bacterie n'est rien, c'est la terrain qui fait tout." Meaning, "Bacteria are nothing, the terrain is everything." The terrain refers to the patient's body, health and resistance.**

We are perpetually surrounded by bacteria and other infectious agents. However, we develop an illness only when our defenses fail to resist the infectious agents. It is very rare that an illness develops in all members of a society. Usually only the weaker or weakened individuals succumb.

During a health professionals' lecture I attended, the presenter, a European MD, stated that he did not allow his children to wash their hands before eating in order to train their immune system to become stronger and more competent.

Although I prefer that kids wash their hands before eating, I support the need to build up our general resistance. Naturally, there are provisions that need to be respected when trying to challenge our immune system. Any reduction in our sanitary habits should be subject to a logical and gradual process, one adapted to each individual.

Weaker individuals, and those with less robust immune or other systems, have to pay more attention to food safety in cooking, storing and serving. This is another reason to promptly eat freshly cooked foods and not use leftovers. As these patients get stronger, they may start relaxing a bit. Those of us who are stronger can be more relaxed about allowing our immune systems to fend off invaders.

This does not mean that we should develop dirty habits and stop paying attention to hygiene and cleanliness. To put what I'm saying into perspective, it is usually sufficient to take the garbage out daily and use mild natural cleaning products. Washing dishes and utensils with mild, natural cleaning products, then drying and putting them away after every meal is more effective than leaving them for a few days and using heavy duty chemicals to get them clean. Using physical means such as a textured cloth, a brush, scouring pads, etc., is far healthier than resorting to chemical agents. It is important to wear gloves when handling even mildly toxic detergents or cleaning agents.

I assume that if you're reading this book, you're well aware that many of today's cleaning/sanitizing agents are considered to be contributing factors in the development of chronic illnesses, allergies and cancers. This is because their toxic residues remain on our dishes, counters, floors, furniture or other objects; they also evaporate into the air we breathe. The chemicals then enter our body via our skin and our digestive and respiratory systems. Children absorb dramatically more toxic residues than adults living in the same environment.

NON-TOXIC TIPS FOR SAFER FOOD HANDLING:

■ MEAT, FISH, POULTRY (MFP):

- Do not thaw and refreeze MFP
- Some meat may be frozen almost indefinitely, but its quality will suffer eventually. This topic is covered well and at length at the following websites:
  - www.foodsafetysite.com
- Freezer burn is not considered a safety hazard; however, depending on the extent of the burn, the quality of the food may be so compromised that it's best to discard it
- Torn wrap is not considered a hazard as long as the meat remained in the freezer; rewrap it as soon as you discover it to retain quality
- For recommended cooking temperatures, visit:
  - www.foodsafetynetwork.ca
  - -click *General Public*
  - -click *In the Home*
- Do not partially pre-cook MFP
- As long as the surface is well cooked, rare or medium-rare MFP should be relatively safe

■ MARINADES:

- If you must use them, do the marinating in the fridge in a fully covered container
- Do not save leftover marinade

■ STUFFING:

- Keep it separate from the meat until ready to use
- Fill the poultry cavity or meat just before roasting
- Do not overfill a poultry cavity – stop at ¾ full
- When poultry or meat is cooked, do not let stuffing sit in the cooked food, remove stuffing while the poultry or meat is cooling

ALWAYS COVER COOKED FOOD

- The longer food is exposed to the air, the more susceptible it is to contamination and oxidization; one of the greatest dangers of contamination occurs during open-air activities such as picnics and potlucks
- Store food in small containers and open them only when required
- Sprinkle compatible culinary herbs over food (many culinary herbs have an antimicrobial effect; see the section *Medicinal Herbs in the Kitchen* for suggestions)
- Cooking destroys most microbial agents. The safest cooking methods are pressure cooking and stir-frying – in that order; other forms, such as high-heat baking, steaming, frying, braising and boiling are also effective

MEAT, FISH AND POULTRY IN THE RAW STATE MUST BE KEPT SEPARATE FROM OTHER FOODS AT ALL TIMES. THIS INCLUDES WHEN:

- *shopping and transporting*
- *preparing*
- *storing*

Pay special attention...

- *do not use the same cutting board, knife and containers for raw meat, fish, poultry, vegetables or other foods*

- *ideally, use one set of cooking utensils for meat, fish and poultry, and another for vegetables and other foods*

- *second best is to wash cooking utensils before you switch foods*

- *pay special attention to cross-contamination due to liquids from meat, either fresh juices or those produced by thawing*

- *after washing the meat, fish or poultry, do not place it into the original container unless it has also been washed*

- *wash the tools used to open the package*

- *wash your hands when switching from handling raw meat, fish or poultry to handling raw vegetables or any other food*

CROSS-CONTAMINATION PREVENTION AND SAFE FOOD STORAGE

■ EGGS

- Leave them in the original carton
- Wash them just before breaking the shell
- If never refrigerated, unwashed organic eggs kept in a cool environment will last several weeks
- Once refrigerated, eggs must always be refrigerated
- Keep them on a refrigerator shelf where it's consistently cold as opposed to in the door of the refrigerator

■ VEGETABLES AND FRUITS

- Wash especially well and cut:
  - tips and stalks
  - indentations or irregularities on the surfaces
  - damaged areas
  - evidence of waxes, pesticides, herbicides (these may be visible or can be felt)
  - if you use a washing agent, rinse well with clean water.
  - Clean using physical means, such as a textured cloth, a brush, scouring pads, etc., combined with a little elbow grease; this is far healthier than resorting to chemical agents
- In general, organically grown foods contain lower amounts of harmful substances, even on the surface; consider spending your money on organic products instead of on cleaning agents

■ GRAINS AND BEANS

- Wash one or more times as required (apart from soil contaminants, fungus tends to grow on grain and bean surfaces)
- The last rinse should be in filtered water
- Store in in glass containers and in a cool dark place

■ FLOURS

- Keep in a tightly closed, preferably glass container in the freezer compartment. Next best is the refrigerator, but use promptly

Note: Even non-toxic cleaning agents may be harmful to the body and trigger adverse reactions; in addition, the body has to process and eliminate them

■ MEAT, FISH, POULTRY

- If you wash meat, fish and poultry, pay special attention to cross-contamination
- Some experts believe MFP should not be washed to decrease the danger of cross-contamination via the spread of microbial agents to other foods, cooking utensils and surfaces
- Defrosted meat, fish and poultry can be kept in the refrigerator in a covered container
- Defrosting should be done in the refrigerator in a covered container or in cold water
    - in order to prevent contamination by water or airborne bacteria, meat has to be kept in a tightly closed plastic bag the whole time. Otherwise, the meat could absorb the water
    - the water must stay cold and must be changed every ½ hour

■ NUTS AND SEEDS

- Keep in their original shells/husks (when the shell/husk is broken, the essential fatty acids rapidly evaporate, and rancidity sets in much faster); that said, many out of shellnuts are sold rancid already
- Store in a cool and dry environment
- If removed from their shell/husk or ground, they must be kept in a tightly closed container (glass), in the refrigerator or freezer

■ OILS AND FATS

- Keep in a cool place and in a dark glass container that's tightly closed
- Butter and other fats should be tightly covered in a preferably glass container and kept in the refrigerator
    - if you prefer to keep butter submerged in water (reduces oxygenation), keep it in a tightly closed glass container
    - alternatively, scrape the butter's surface with a knife, discard the scrapings and clean the knife; then use the fresh surface

NOTES ON REFRIGERATION AND FREEZING:

- *meats and other foods should be frozen as rapidly as possible*
- *if applicable, cut the meat into thinner portions, wrap, and spread out in the freezer until fully frozen*
- *keep all food items in closed glass or other containers to:*
    - *prevent the spread of spores/fungus*
    - *reduce humidity in the fridge*
    - *prevent exposure to fridge or freezer air since refrigerant is toxic*

■ STORING CONTAINERS

- Some clay containers contain high amounts of heavy metals that can leach into the food (this is often the case with imported products; Buyer Beware)
- Plastic bags and containers contain exogenous estrogens.
  - the softer the plastic, the warmer and more acidic the environment, the greater potential for estrogens to be released into foods
- Glass containers appear to be the healthiest choice since they release only minute amounts of silica
- Stainless steel might also be acceptable, but comparatively less so than glass. Beware of aluminum and heavy-metal content.
  - look for verifiably stainless steel products. Buyer Beware applies here. Do not be misled by US or Canadian trademarks – the products may have been produced elsewhere

IDEAS FOR QUICK MEALS, SNACKS AND BREAKFASTS

14

This chapter is intended to provide ideas, inspirations and recipes to prepare a quick health-promoting meal. You'll see that it doesn't take long to makes a tasty, nutritious meal that will not aggravate your condition.

Only three pages, just take a quick look, make your pick, and start.

CHAPTERS THAT CONTAIN HELPFUL RECIPES FOR QUICK MEALS

FOODS AND COOKING TIPS TO CONSIDER

BEAN SPROUTS, FRESH STRING BEANS, LENTILS/DHALS

Bean sprouts and fresh string beans can be used by those who are not sensitive to them. Bean sprouts need less than a minute to Stir-fry, steam or cook. Fresh beans require a bit more time.

Dry lentils/dhal or small beans, require soaking before cooking and a longer time to cook than fresh beans. Small Dhal, Pink or French lentils or black beans cook faster than other beans.

BEVERAGES

Tea and alternative milk (oat, rice, nut or seed milk), water from boiled or steamed vegetables or fruits.

BREAD SUBSTITUTION

Non-wheat, non-corn flat breads, buns, crackers, tortillas, cakes, pancakes, wraps and crêpes.

Pre-make dough or batter and keep it in the fridge. It takes only a few minutes to make tortillas, flat breads, pancakes or crackers if the dough or batter is ready. (This is a healthier alternative to commercially produced breads).

COLD SNACKS/MEALS

If you must have a cold snack, like pre-made non-wheat or non-corn tortillas, crackers, or flatbreads, drink warm tea or alternative milk to warm up your digestion. Those of us whose digestion is very weak may need to soak or dip crackers in soup, tea, sauce, or milk alternative to soften them.

EGGS

Eggs contain a complete protein and are easy and fast to prepare in various ways. They can be made into spreads, quick omelettes or added to the cooking at the last minute, (e.g. soups, porridges, steamed or stir-fried vegetables).

MEAT

Meat can be anything from organic stew/hamburger meat to turkey, chicken, fish or organic sausages. Don't eat preserved deli sausages or meats.

Use minced meat, or meat, poultry, fish cut to smaller pieces; do not overcook.

Pre-cut the meat and mix it with seasonings ahead of time so it's ready when you need it.

NUTS/SEEDS

Ground or/and stir-fried nuts and seeds can be used instead of meat or in addition to it. Presuming that you are not sensitive to them.

ONE DISH COOKING

One-dish meals can be done very effectively when using a pressure cooker, slow cooker or the Korean Cuckoo. Cuckoo is a program-mable rice pressure cooker that can be used for other grains. Check the manufacturer's safety standards and warrantees.

PORRIDGES

Rolled oat, rye, barley, quinoa or amaranth flakes, and puffed millet cook in minutes. Unfortunately they have a lower nutritional value than their whole grain counterparts. See *Quick Roasted Porridge from Any Grain.*

SPREADS

Nut, seed, bean, avocado, egg, fish.

Nut and seed butters can be pre-made and kept in a refrigerator. Avocado and egg spreads are quick to make and should be made fresh if possible.

Spreads can be served with far more than the usual bread or crackers. They are excellent over steamed vegetables or mixed in with porridges, beans, pancakes...

SOUPS

Soup or stew can cook while you are putting on your makeup or shaving. Vegetable soup with quinoa or buckwheat with some chopped meat or eggs, does not take much time at all.

Quick soups are easy to make. Just start with the ingredient which takes the longest to cook and gradually add those that take less time to cook. For instance, start with fast-cooking beans and grains, then spices, and finally meat and vegetables. Beans, slow-cooking grain and bones take longer to cook, but make the soup heartier. If you really do not have the time, use only vegetables and eggs or meat, but don't forget the seasonings, if not irritating.

STIR-FRYING OR STEAMING

These can provide a complete meal in minutes. Just use vegetables and some source of protein.

TASTE PROMOTERS

Do not be afraid to experiment with culinary herbs and spices, but avoid pre-made and premixed condiments.

VEGETABLES

Stir-frying or steaming vegetables takes two to three minutes.

The healthiest choice is fresh vegetables that are cut just before cooking.

The second best is commercially pre-cut frozen vegetables. They are the fastest to prepare. Due to the flash freezing process used, these may have more vitamins than 'fresh' vegetables that have been sitting on shelves an unspecified length of time. Either way, it's a big step in the right direction.

Do not forget to add a sprinkle of salt when cooking vegetables to enhance flavour and sweetness.

COMBINATIONS

Combine any of the following:

Vegetables, fruits, breads, buns, crackers, tortillas, cakes, pancakes, crêpes and porridges, with a protein source such as beans, meat, poultry, fish, nuts, seeds or eggs. This includes nut and seed butters and their milks.

Stir-fried, cooked, or steamed vegetables with a protein food such as scrambled eggs or omelettes. Both can be eaten with pancakes, tortillas or flatbread. Do not use breads containing wheat or corn.

Grain products can be included, but are not necessary if the meal contains enough vegetables.

There is no need to make a snack or quick meal into a major operation. Just ensure that you combine a source of protein (meat, poultry, fish, eggs, nuts, seeds or beans) with either vegetables, grains, beans (or all of them).

Do not discard cooking water from steaming or boiling produce. Drink it with or without additional flavouring or make it into a soup. Simply return the cooked vegetables and meat to the water along with your favourite seasonings, then heat and serve.

Do not be afraid to be creative and adventurous with your food.

The taste of any dish can be varied with a simple change of seasonings. Use them according to your taste or their medicinal benefits. Green herbs are usually added during the last 10 to 15 minutes of cooking. The more colourful spices can be added much earlier, even at the beginning of cooking.

The most effective taste promoters are sautéed or browned onion and garlic. Start with them before adding liquid or anything else. They also provide a pleasant aroma that improves production of digestive juices.

If you find you are still hungry, increase your food intake and/or increase the amount of fat in your diet – nuts, seeds, butter or oils like fish oil or flaxseed oil are excellent choices provided you tolerate them.

If you are hypoglycemic, make certain you have proteins and fats in every meal – obviously, no junk or simple sugars.

TIPS FOR MORNINGS MADE EASY

Do all the prep work the night before. Divide and place all the ingredients on a covered tray or in a large container and store overnight in the fridge.

Use a slow cooker. Fill the cooker and start the timer so the recipes will be done when you get up in the morning.

Use a pressure cooker for one-dish cooking. Just load it up and turn it on and off as required.

In the worst-case scenario use wheat- and corn-free crackers, tortillas or bread with spreads and warm alternative milk or tea. Ideally, breakfast should be the largest meal, but even a little change will help your health and energy levels.

Note: All recipes can be doubled or tripled as required. Ideally, make enough for one meal with no leftovers or cook enough for the next meal and keep it warm in a thermos. Preheat the thermos by pouring boiling water into it, then close it and let stand for a few minutes. Empty the water and immediately refill it with the hot food.

BEVERAGES TO 'KEEP HEALTHY'

COFFEE SUBSTITUTES

Although the best substitute for caffeine is probably a power-nap, some people find it hard to give up their java. There are many organic substitutes on the market to help kick the habit. Caf-lib™, Teecchino™, Cafix™, Caffree™, Inka™, Raja's Cup™, Roma™, Roastaroma™. Herbal teas: bamboo, chicory, dandelion, or collinsonia (which must be cooked for a long period of time).

FRUIT DRINKS AND SYRUPS

ROB'S CRANBERRY 'COOL'-AID
Tastes good warm.

1 c. cranberries, fresh or frozen
3 c. or more of filtered water
½ t. or to taste, stevia, sucanat, licorice or other recommended sweetener

- In a medium saucepan, cook the cranberries in just enough filtered water to facilitate boiling until the berries start to burst
- Transfer hot mixture to blender and liquefy at high speed while adding hot/warm water until the desired consistency is reached
- Add sweetener
- Serve at a warm sipping temperature

BERRY OR FRUIT DELIGHT
If you just can't live without fruit shakes.

Base
1 c. pure unsweetened coconut milk
Optional: 1 to 2 t. rice syrup, if more sweetness is desired

Flavourings
½ c. cooked pineapple in its own juice, fresh strawberries, raspberries or blueberries or other recommended fruits

- Cook the berries or fruits briefly; do not overcook or they will lose their texture and sweetness
- Immediately transfer to a blender

ABBREVIATIONS
c. = cup
T. = Tablespoon
t. = teaspoon

THE BEST BEVERAGES ARE FILTERED WARM WATER AND MILD HERBAL TEAS.

Variation:
Make stevia or licorice tea and use it in place of the sweetened water. This not only tastes great, it increases the amount of beneficial herbs in the drink.

AVOID EATING RAW FRUIT IF YOU HAVE VERY WEAK DIGESTION.

- Adjust the thickness by adding hot filtered water while you blend
- Warm the ingredients to a pleasant sipping temperature

RACHAEL'S CHOCOLA SYRUP
For those of us who can't resist chocolate.

1 c. cocoa or carob powder (unsweetened)
2 c. sweetener (rice syrup or barley malt)
¼ t. salt
1 c. cold water
1 t. vanilla

- Mix cocoa and sugar until evenly blended
- Add salt and water and mix well until smooth
- Warm the mixture over medium heat
- Gradually bring to a boil and keep boiling until thickened, stirring to prevent boil-over
- Remove from heat and let cool
- When mixture is cool, add vanilla.
  Use for chocolate milk, hot cocoa, or a topping

Note: *Those with strong digestion may use fresh uncooked berries in their shake provided it is warmed to a sipping temperature after blending.*

" Among other health concerns I used to feel sick every time after I ate. When I started Dr. Kodet's nutritional regimen, I can say that if my stomach was like a cat, it would be purring after every meal. **"**

– Mokgoshi Tumisang

CHILDREN'S FORMULAS
AND MILK SUBSTITUTES

16

CHILDREN'S FORMULAS

OPTION ONE:
- 1 c. alternative milk (or broth/purée e.g. vegetable and meat or bone broth. You also can use two kinds of broth/purée instead of a milk alternative.)
- 1 c. vegetable broth
- 1 t. flax or other seeds (ground and soaked) or ⅓ t. or more oil, rich in Essential Fatty Acids
- **Optional:** 1 t. rice syrup or barley malt.

NOTE: Make a point to reduce your child's reliance on sweet tastes.

BROTH OR PURÉE:

- Boil or steam vegetables of your choice until very soft (squash, rutabaga, broccoli)
- Drain and reserve the water
- Add the flax or other seeds (ground and soaked) to the vegetable water
- If a thicker consistency is desired (such as for older babies), mash enough cooked veggies to equal ⅓ cup and blend with all the other ingredients
- Pour ingredients into blender and blend until smooth

CHILDREN AND EFAS

Children require more Essential Fatty Acids (EFAs) than adults. Consider adding a bit of one of the following organic non-GMO products to the milks:

- flaxseed • walnut • pumpkin seed • hemp • cold water fish oil • evening primrose oil (EPO) • borage • black currant oil

IMPORTANT NOTES:

- *DO NOT USE unpasteurized honey for children under one year old*
- *Strain formula if child is less than 7 kg/15.4 lbs. or if younger than 6 months*
- *If using these formulas in a baby bottle, increase the diameter of the nipple hole by either cutting with sterilized scissors or drilling with a sterilized drill bit*
- *Store these alternative milks refrigerated in a glass container with a tight-fitting lid for a maximum of two days*
- ***Children who are sensitive to soy or dairy (cow and goat milk products) may react adversely to any of the nut, or seed-based milk substitutes***
- *Introduce these milks and formulas slowly, increasing new milk ratios only if there are no adverse reactions noted*
- *Focus on finding compatible milk alternatives and keep rotating/changing them*
- *Nuts and seeds may be too difficult for a sensitive child. Vegetable or bone/meat broths may be easier choices*

DISCONTINUE IF THE CHILD STARTS EXHIBITING ANY ADVERSE REACTIONS AND DO NOT ATTEMPT TO BUILD "TOLERANCE" BY INCREASING THE AMOUNT OR CONCENTRATION OF THE OFFENDING MILK ALTERNATIVE.

DO NOT BE AFRAID TO EXPERIMENT WITH OTHER NUTS AND SEEDS.

Tip: *Soaking seeds or nuts overnight begins the sprouting process, which increases the nutrients in the water and softens the seeds/nuts for better blending. Blend the seeds or nuts immediately in the soaking water. If the child is very sensitive, drain and replace the original water with fresh water.*

Some of these milks will not have a familiar taste. Yet, they will provide a unique and pleasant taste when used as a milk substitute in cooking.

Lactate, lactic acid and lact-albumin don't contain lactose.

INFANTS:
There is no substitute for breast milk. Ideally, do not discontinue breastfeeding before your baby reaches one year old. In addition, nursing has some cancer-protective effects for the mother.

*Based on my experience, **if a child is reacting nega-tively to mother's milk, it is almost exclusively due to the mother's diet.** The child's and the mother's condition normally improves within days of my treating both of them. The nutri-tional changes required are described in this book and always play a key role.*

MILK SUBSTITUTES

For babies and the rest of us who need to treat our systems with love and care.

• almond milk • brazil nut milk • cashew milk • coconut milk (fresh or made from dried coconut) • hazelnut milk • hemp milk • oat milk • quinoa milk • rice milk (includes Amazake) • sesame seed milk • sunflower seed milk (use caution, due to potential sensitivities)

INSTANT NUT OR SEED MILK
1 c. nuts or seeds
2 to 3 c. or more hot filtered water, depending on viscosity desired
Optional:
  sweeteners such as:
  1 t. of either: brown rice syrup, barley malt syrup, sorghum molasses, date sugar, honey, maple syrup, puréed cooked fruits,
  spices or flavouring such as:
  ¼ t. of either allspice, cloves, cinnamon or vanilla

• Pulverize the nuts or seeds in a grinder or blender (immediately before using to reduce loss of healthy essential fatty acids)
• Transfer ground product to a blender
• Add the spices and/or sweeteners
• Gradually pour hot water to the mixture and blend till smooth
Optional: Strain through a fine sieve or cheesecloth

BROWN RICE MILK
1 c. brown rice, sweet brown rice, or a blend of both
5 to 10 c. water
pinch of salt
Optional: 1 t. butter

• Wash and drain the rice
• If using, melt the butter over medium heat in a large, thick-bottomed pot or heavy frying pan
• Add rice and stir until the rice starts to pop
  • This step can be done without butter, just watch carefully to avoid scorching, reducing heat if necessary
• Slowly pour in water, then add salt
• Reduce heat and simmer, stirring occasionally for two hours
  • add water if required
• Remove from heat and strain through a fine sieve or cheesecloth
• Use the rice cream, leftover in the sieve, with other foods

OAT MILK FROM WHOLE OATS

1 c. whole oats
5 c. warm or cool water

- Soak overnight in cold water in a covered container, in either the refrigerator or a cool environment
- Blend while slowly adding filtered water until the desired consistency is reached
- Heat to desired drinking temperature
  - **Note:** for small children and very sensitive patients simmer briefly while stirring
- If required, store in refrigerator for maximum of two days before serving.

Optional: for a sweeter taste: add ½ t. brown rice syrup or barley malt

OAT MILK FROM OATMEAL PORRIDGE

1 c. slow cooking rolled oats. Use a one to two oats to water ratio.

Optional:
    ¼ t. cinnamon
    ¼ t. vanilla extract
    ½ t. rice syrup, barley malt or ¼ t. licorice powder
    ¼ t. salt

- Add the oats, optional flavourings if using, and salt to the boiling water and stir
- Reduce heat to simmer, cover and cook until oatmeal is soft, stirring occasionally
  - **Optional:** cover, remove from heat and let stand for a few minutes until desired level of doneness is reached
- Eat the blend as a deliciously flavoured porridge or continue to make oat milk by transfering to a blender and blending to a desired consistency, while gradually adding hot water

FOR ALL MILKS:
Use cold water for both soaking and blending if refrigerating the milk.

Use cold water for soaking and hot water for blending if consuming immediately.

Note: The optional ingredients should be adapted to your individual tastes and sensitivities. For example, some of us react adversely to licorice.

Tip: More experienced cooks boil the water first and carefully pour the quinoa into the water in small amounts while stirring with a whisk to prevent lumps and avoid scorching.

Tip: Consider
making nut milk from a
combination of two or more
nuts to which you do not
have an adverse reaction.
Add this combination to
your favourite tea
(e.g. almond milk and
hazelnut milk added to
rooibos chai tea).

Caution: You might
react to the combination of
the two nuts, even if you do
not react to either of them
separately.

QUINOA MILK

1 c. quinoa
6 c. water

- Wash, drain and dry quinoa
- Grind quinoa in a coffee grinder or blender to make a flour
- Heat the water and while stirring with a whisk, carefully pour the quinoa flour into the water in small amounts to prevent lumps and avoid scorching
- While stirring constantly, bring to a boil, turn heat down and simmer about 10 minutes
- let stand for 5 minutes and then strain through a cheesecloth

CASHEW MILK

1 c. cashews
3 c. or more, filtered water

- Rinse nuts well
- Soak nuts in the water overnight, preferably in a glass bowl
- Drain nuts and reserve the water
- Place nuts in blender and, starting with one cup of the reserved water, blend at high speed
- Add more water as required to reach the desired milky consistency
- Strain the blended milk for younger children
- If sweetening is necessary, add the rice syrup during blending
- Warm the milk to the proper serving temperature, stirring constantly

Optional: rice syrup or barley malt to taste; use sweeteners in moderation

SESAME SEED MILK

2 T. raw whole sesame seeds
3 c. or more filtered water

- Wash the sesame seeds and soak them in filtered water for 2 to 8 hours, preferably in a glass container; the longer the seeds are soaked, the softer they become
- Drain seeds and reserve the water
- Place seeds in blender and, starting with one cup of the reserved water, blend at high speed
- Add more water as required to reach the desired consistency
- Strain the blended milk for younger children
- If sweetening is necessary, add the rice syrup during blending
- Warm the milk to the proper serving temperature, stirring constantly

Optional: rice syrup or barley malt to taste; use sweeteners in moderation

ALMOND MILK

1 c. raw almonds
3 c. or more filtered water

- Wash and soak almonds overnight in the water, ideally in a covered glass container
- Drain nuts and reserve the water
- Manually remove the almond skins and discard
- Place nuts in blender and, starting with one cup of the reserved water (heated if necessary), blend at high speed
- Add more water as required to reach the desired milky consistency
- Strain the blend for younger children
- If sweetening is necessary, add the rice syrup during blending
- Warm the milk to the proper serving temperature, stirring constantly

Optional: 1 to 3 t. rice syrup; avoid if possible or use in moderation

COCONUT MILK

3 to 4 c. dry, shredded unsweetened coconut
5 c. boiling filtered water

- Fill a four-cup measuring cup with the coconut
- Pour boiling water over the coconut and fill to the top
- Cover with four layers of cheesecloth large enough to overhang an inch or so on each side of the container
- Let stand until the mixture cools to warm
- While squeezing the coconut in the cheesecloth, drain as much of the milk as you can into a bowl or container
- Leave the residual coconut in the measuring cup and repeat the process; the second straining will yield a thinner milk

Both the first and the second milk can be combined and used as a coconut milk or used to make coconut butter. Or, use the second straining as a coconut milk and the first for butter. The residual coconut may be added to coconut rice or soups.

COCONUT BUTTER/OIL
- Complete the process for coconut milk, but refrigerate the milk
- The oil will rise to the top and harden
- Remove this top layer and use as coconut oil or butter

SOYBEAN MILK
1 c. soybeans
4 c. filtered water

- Wash soybeans and soak in a large amount of water for two days, changing the water several times
- Drain and place soybeans in blender and blend at high speed until finely ground. If smaller blender is used, blend in small batches
- Transfer ground soybeans to a large pot and add 4 or more cups of water
- Gradually bring to a boil over medium-high heat, stirring occasionally
- Reduce heat and simmer for 20 to 40 minutes, stirring occasionally
- Pour through a strainer or, if for a small child, pour through cheesecloth and twist to express the milk
- Repeat the process to yield a second thinner milk; pour 2 c. of boiling water in with the pulp, simmer and strain again
- Supplement with breast milk for infants, or other food for older children

Note: I do not advocate extensive use of non-fermented soy products such as soy milk. If you have to have it, soy milk made at home is healthier than that bought in the store.

CRASH COURSE IN NUTS AND SEEDS

17

CRASH COURSE IN NUT AND SEED ROASTING

JANICE'S SLOW ROASTED NUTS AND SEEDS
This is the gourmet, slow-roast approach to making your own roasted nuts at home. Try it once and you'll be spoiled!

■ Crispy Almonds
4 c. organic almonds
1 t. sea salt
Filtered water to cover

■ Crispy Pecans or Walnuts
4 c. pecan halves or walnuts
2 t. sea salt
Filtered water to cover

■ Crispy Cashews
4 c. organic "raw" cashews
1 t. sea salt
Filtered water to cover

■ Pepitas
4 c. raw, hulled organic pumpkin seeds
2 t. sea salt
1 t. cayenne pepper
Filtered water to cover

Procedure for all recipes:

- Soak in filtered water and Celtic sea salt overnight, or for 7 hours
- Drain nuts well and scatter onto a cookie sheet
- Dry roast in the lowest oven possible, for 12 to 24 hours
- Most 170˚F ovens only require the 12-hour roasting time
- At the 12-hour mark, cool a sample and taste-test it

FAST-TRACK ROASTED NUTS AND SEEDS
Experiment with a variety of nuts and seeds – you may be surprised by the superior taste of freshly roasted nuts and seeds.

Desired amount of seeds or nuts (pumpkin seeds, sesame seeds, unprocessed almonds, cashews)
Optional: Add butter or coconut oil

- Roast the nuts or seeds in a clean, dry, cast iron frying pan over medium heat; cover the pan bottom
- Keep stirring to avoid burning
- If using butter, pay extra attention to prevent burning; remember that clarified butter can take more heat
  - Add the butter toward the end, just after you turn off the heat; do not forget to stir, since the pan will retain heat and continue roasting
- Season with spices and salt if desired

Note:
Do not soak cashews longer than 6 hours

Cashews must be baked at 200˚F; otherwise, they become slimy and inedible

STORAGE:
Store walnuts in the fridge in an airtight container

All other nuts and pumpkin seeds can be stored at room temperature for months in an airtight container

REFRIGERATE NUT BUTTERS
You won't believe the difference in the taste of a batch of fresh roasted nuts; grind some into nut butter as well, but make up small amounts to ensure the freshest taste

NUT AND SEED BUTTERS

FLAVOURED, TOASTED ALMONDS
There's virtually no limit to the ways you can season almonds, one of the healthiest nuts around. This recipe may be used for other nuts as well.

1½ c. almonds
¼ t. cumin, turmeric, or curry
dash of salt
Optional: 4 T. organic butter, clarified organic butter, coconut butter or coconut oil

- Preheat a dry, heavy pan or a heavy skillet to medium heat
- Toast almonds without any oil or butter
- When almost done, turn the heat off or reduce to low
- If using butter or oil, stir in the butter or oil when the pan is at the lower temperature
- Transfer the nuts and seasonings to a glass jar with a well-fitting lid and shake to distribute

NUT AND SEED BUTTERS
2 c. roasted or raw nuts/seeds
½ c. organic coconut or other oil
1 t. sea salt (optional)

- Place nuts and salt in a food processor and grind to a fine powder
- Add sweetener (if using)
- Drizzle in the coconut oil
  - Add oil gradually until the desired texture is achieved
- Process until smooth; butter will be firm when chilled
- Store in an airtight container in the refrigerator

NUT AND SEED BUTTERS SIMPLY
2 c. roasted or raw nuts/seeds
2 T. organic coconut or other oil

- Place nuts in a food processor and grind to a fine powder
- Drizzle in oil and process until smooth; Butter will be firm when chilled
- Store in an airtight container in the refrigerator

FOR ALL BUTTERS:
- *For sweet taste add 1 - 2 T. rice syrup or barley malt when adding the oil*
- *For savoury taste add ½ t. spices of your choice, when adding the oil*
- *Let stand for an hour or longer for the spice flavour to blend*

ALMOND BUTTER
If you'd like a change from sugared Pea-butter™, the commercial alternative to peanut butter made with chickpeas, try another nut you're not allergic to and whip up a batch! We love this almond version.

1 c. blanched almonds
1 t. olive oil or non-genetically modified organic canola or flaxseed oil
1 t. rice syrup to taste
salt to taste
water as needed to blend

- Place almonds in a food processor and blend until floury, shaking the container to ensure a consistent grind
- Drizzle in oil while blending, then repeat with the rice syrup
- If the mixture is too thick, add small amounts of water

SESAME SEED BUTTER
1½ c. roasted or raw sesame seeds
¼ c. organic sesame seed or other oil or organic butter
Optional: 1 t. rice syrup or barley malt or sea salt

- Roast sesame seeds in a frying pan until golden (if using roasted seeds)
- Place seeds in a food processor and grind to a fine powder
- Add sweetener or salt, if using
- Drizzle in the sesame seed oil
- Process until smooth
- Butter will be firm when chilled
- Store in an airtight container in the refrigerator

NUT AND SEED CEREAL TOPPING

COCONUT AND NUT CEREAL TOPPING
1 T. pure unsweetened coconut
¼ c. whole cashews or other nuts
dash of salt

- Pulse ingredients in a food processor just before eating to preserve the essential fatty acids in the nuts
- Serve as a topping for cereal, porridge, pancakes, etc
- **Optional:** Add a small drizzle of rice syrup (preferred) or maple syrup (in a pinch)

POPPY SEED CEREAL TOPPING
Very European

½ c. poppy seeds
½ c. milk alternative
Optional (any or all of the following):
    2 T. butter or flax oil or other oil (organic)
    2 T. fruit dry crushed or fresh berries (if you can tolerate fresh fruit)
    or 1 T. rice syrup or barley malt
    1 t. vanilla

- Grind poppy seeds in a coffee grinder or in a blender
- Transfer to a bowl
- Add all other ingredients and mix with a fork
- Let sit for a few minutes for the seeds to soften
- Serve on top or blend into hot oatmeal/porridge

PIQUANT SESAME SEED BUTTER
1½ c. roasted or raw sesame seeds
¼ c. organic sesame or other oil or organic butter
4 t. mustard seeds
1 T. parsley, dry
1 t. rosemary, dry

- Roast sesame seeds in a frying pan until golden (if using roasted seeds)
- Place all ingredients, except for oil, in a food processor and grind to a fine powder
- Drizzle in oil
- Process until smooth
- Let stand an hour for the flavour to blend
- Butter will be firm when chilled
- Store in an airtight container in the refrigerator

Tip: Use these same approaches with other seeds.

MAYONNAISE, MUSTARD, GARLIC OIL AND DRESSINGS

18

WARNING: WHEN USING RAW EGG YOLKS VERIFY THE SOURCE OF THE EGGS.
I am not persuaded that cooked mayonnaise is much safer, since it is not cooked at high enough temperature to destroy salmonella and other pathogens.

Warning: Mustard is a goitrogen that has a suppressive effect on the thyroid. Those with severe hypothyroidism should avoid mustard. Cooking inactivates goitrogens, so cooked mustard greens or seeds are fine.

Mustard tastes even better the second or third day after it's made. Since it's so easy to prepare, there is no need to make and store large amounts.

MAYONNAISE WITH OR WITHOUT GARLIC
2 organic egg yolks
1 c. oil (choice of olive, flax or other oils)
1 T. vinegar (white wine vinegar)
or 1-3 garlic cloves crushed to a paste
1 T. warm water
¼ t. salt
¼ t. mustard seeds finely ground
pinch black pepper

- In a bowl whisk the egg yolks
- Add all the solid ingredients and ½ teaspoon of oil
- Whisk till smooth
- While whisking, add the rest of the oil in a slow drizzle
- Mix in the vinegar or garlic at the end

MUSTARD
This recipe is from one of my most experienced advisors, Irene Veselic, who was a professional cook her whole life. Now in her eighties, she is cooking according to this book.

½ c. (or less) dry mustard powder
6 T. vinegar of your choice
2 T. hot water

Some of us like to add various ingredients to mustard. Popular choices include:

- horseradish • honey • garlic • onions • thyme • dill • basil • brown or black mustard seeds • sesame seeds

Ingredients such as horseradish make the mustard stronger tasting. Honey or sesame seeds make it milder.

- Choose a jar large enough to contain the finished mustard recipe
- Pour in mustard powder
- While stirring, gradually add the liquids, alternating between the vinegar and the hot water
- When you are close to the desired consistency, taste the mixture
- If required, add vinegar or hot water to taste, or to thin the mustard a bit more

Store in the refrigerator and use just before serving, or add to recipes at the very end of cooking.

GARLIC OIL

10 cloves garlic, crushed and finely minced
½ to 1 litre glass bottle of olive oil
Optional: 1 t. to 1 T. oregano if you are into Greek cooking,
or 1 t. to 1 T. basil for a more Italian flavour.

* Add garlic to the bottle of olive oil
* Add herbs, if using
* Tightly close the bottle, shake and store in a cool place away
  from light
* Strain before serving

HORSERADISH AND ONION DRESSING

1 c. organic, non-GMO flaxseed or hemp seed oil
2 t. horseradish, finely minced
2 t. green onion, finely minced
1 to 2 T. balsamic vinegar or lemon juice (if tolerated)
Optional: 2 cloves garlic, crushed and finely minced

* Mix all the ingredients together and pour into a glass bottle
* Close tightly, shake well, and let stand for a few hours

ANYTHING GOES DRESSING

1 c. oil of your choice (e.g. non-GMO organic flaxseed,
olive, walnut)
2 cloves garlic, crushed and finely minced
Optional: 1 t. horseradish, finely minced
½ t. thyme or rosemary
½ t. oregano or marjoram
½ t. basil or parsley
1 T. balsamic vinegar or 1 to 2 T. lemon juice (if not sensitive)
salt to taste

Purists avoid blending due to concerns that high-speed
blending damages food and reduces its nutritional value.
Choose your method below:

No-blender method:

* Hand-crush and mince garlic and horseradish
* Mix all the ingredients together, including garlic and horseradish
* Pour into a glass jar, close tightly, shake well and let stand for
  a few hours
* Spices may be adapted to your taste and tolerance

Tip: It may take two or more days for the garlic to infuse the oil. However, do not store garlic oil longer than a few weeks as it may start fermenting.

Hint: If you prefer to reduce the amount of oil, replace ½ c. oil with ½ c. tahini.

DRESSINGS CAN BE MADE IN ADVANCE AND KEPT IN THE FRIDGE FOR A FEW DAYS

* *Try them on meats, fish, eggs, grains, beans and cooked vegetables.*

* *If your digestion is strong, use dressings on raw salads made from softer vegetables. The warming effect of the dressing will balance the cooling effect of the raw vegetables.*

* *Oil must be added in a slow drizzle during whisking or blending for best results.*

Blender method:

• Put <u>all</u> ingredients into the blender and blend
• Pour into a glass bottle and let stand for a few hours
• Spices may be added to reflect your taste and tolerance

TANGY MAYO DRESSING
1 c. organic mayonnaise
¼ t. turmeric or curry powder
¼ t. paprika with pinch of pepper
1 to 2 cloves garlic
½ t. ginger
1 T. balsamic vinegar or lemon juice
salt to taste
Optional: pinch of cinnamon or a pinch of mustard powder
(if not aggravating)

• Whisk all the ingredients together
• Adjust spices to taste
• If too tangy, add mayo or oil and mix again
• Store in a glass container in the fridge

SPREADS, DIPS, LIVER PÂTÉ AND SANDWICH FILLINGS

19

AVOCADO EGG SPREAD

1 avocado
1 medium-hard boiled egg
1 to 2 T. sesame seed butter or mayonnaise
2 T. chopped fresh cilantro or parsley
1 to 2 green onions, finely chopped (use entire onion with greens) or 1T. finely chopped chives
1 clove garlic, chopped and crushed
1 t. lemon juice or vinegar
paprika, black pepper and salt to taste
pinch of mustard powder (if not irritating)

- Boil the egg until medium hard; cut the egg in half; carefully scoop out contents
- Wash the avocado
- Cut avocado lengthwise, open and discard pit
- Either scoop out flesh, or peel skin from flesh if not using skins as serving bowls
- Dice the egg and avocado
- Using fork or blender, mix and mash the avocado, egg and all other ingredients
- Adjust seasonings to taste
- Serve in the avocado skins as a side dish, or as a spread or dip

AVOCADO SALMON SPREAD

Follow the recipe for *Avocado Egg Spread* but replace the egg with a comparable amount of cooked salmon (stir-fried, boiled or steamed). Add a pinch or two of dill.

AVOCADO SPREAD

This recipe can be prepared with different seasonings, depending on your taste preferences. For example, try powdered spices such as pepper, paprika, caraway seeds, cumin or coriander, to name a few. Lemon juice also may be added to taste, if you are not sensitive to it.

1 avocado
1 clove garlic, crushed
(omit if sensitive to)
salt to taste
other seasonings to taste

- Wash the avocado
- Cut avocado lengthwise, remove flesh, discard pit and reserve the skin
- Mix flesh with seasonings and garlic
- Refill avocado skins and serve as a side dish, or as a spread or dip

DO NOT COOK AVOCADO

Tips: *In lieu of adding lemon juice, leave the avocado pit in with the mixture to prevent browning. Stir occasionally.*

Don't worry if you're missing some of the ingredients. Avocado tastes good with almost anything.

WHOLE EGG SPREAD
3 hard-boiled eggs
1 small onion or leek, finely chopped
3 T. mayonnaise
salt and pepper to taste
lemon juice or balsamic vinegar to taste, if not sensitive
Optional: ¼ c. of daikon or 3 small radishes, steamed or boiled

- Hard boil the eggs:
  - Method 1: start them in cold water and boil for 8 minutes from the start of boiling
  - Method 2: carefully place eggs into boiling water and boil for 10 to 12 minutes
- Steam or sauté onion/leek
- Peel eggs and blend or mash them with all other ingredients
- Garnish with any green herb

Serve warm as you would any other spread with almost anything: vegetables, crackers, wheat-free bread, grains, beans. Or, spread onto large slightly steamed lettuce leaves and roll up. Great as a filling for baked zucchini, squash, rutabaga etc.

GARNISH IDEAS:
- *Use fresh coriander (cilantro) as a garnish*
- *Parsley is also a nice garnish, for very sensitive people, steam the fresh cilantro or parsley*
- *A sprinkle of ground sesame or pumpkin seeds, or a drizzle of their butters adds a delicious flavour*

BEAN SPREAD/DIP
You'll find many uses for this versatile tasty purée.

½ c. dry black beans (or other beans, chickpeas, green or split peas, lentils or dhal)
culinary herbs and spices to your taste (e.g. coriander, cumin)
1 clove garlic, minced
1 small onion, minced
¼ t. pepper and paprika, or to your taste/tolerance
½ t. salt, or to taste
½ to 1 t. butter

- Soak the beans/legumes for several hours or overnight, changing the water a few times (as described in *Beans Crash Course*)
- Immerse beans/legumes in four times as much fresh water as the volume of the beans/legumes
- Bring to a boil, skim off foam, reduce heat to simmer and cook the legumes to half done
- Strain and replace the water with fresh water
- Add cumin and coriander and simmer legumes until soft
- Purée in a blender or food processor
- Melt the butter in a frying pan large and deep enough to hold the entire recipe
- Sauté the minced garlic and onion in butter for two minutes
- Pour in the puréed beans, pepper, paprika and salt
- Cook, while stirring, for a few more minutes
- Serve in a wide bowl or small platter for dipping, or sneak it into your favourite wraps, etc., as a nutritious spread

EASY BEAN SPREAD/DIP
If the previous recipe is too involved, or the ingredients too allergenic, keep it simple with this dip.

½ c. dry black beans (or other beans, peas, lentils or dhal)
1 small finely chopped onion (only use if not sensitive to)
salt to taste

- Soak the beans/legumes for several hours or overnight, changing the water a few times (as described in the section *Beans Crash Course*)

- Immerse beans in four times as much fresh water as the volume of the legumes
- Bring to a boil, skim off foam, reduce heat to simmer and cook the legumes to half done
- Strain and replace the water with fresh water
- Cook the legumes until soft
- Add the salt and onion in the last few minutes of cooking
- Mash the cooked beans
- If more flavour is desired, mix in any or all of the following:
    - seasonings of your choice
    - avocado (very few people react adversely to avocado, but always be mindful when adding foods)
    - miso paste (if you are certain you can tolerate it)
    - cooked and mashed vegetables (e.g. radish family, or any vegetables of your choice.)

HUMMUS (CHICKPEA DIP)
Quick and simple to whip up in a food processor.

1 lb. to 1¼ lb. cooked chickpeas (for cooking instructions, see the *Crash Course in Beans and Legumes*
¼ to 1c. tahini (sesame seed paste)
2 to 4 garlic cloves
½ t. salt
¼ c. lemon juice, grapefruit juice (if not sensitive to it) or tart fruit juice, such as cranberry.
Substitutions for tart juices: approx 1 T. vinegar (taste before adding more) or a small amount of fresh seaweed

- Place all ingredients in a food processor or blender
- Blend to a smooth paste; usually takes about 2 or 3 minutes
- You may drizzle in a little water to help the blending and make a thinner dip, if desired
- Traditionally, hummus is served on a small platter sprinkled with extra virgin olive oil and parsley sprigs, or try green onions sliced thinly
- Scoop up with your favourite wheat-free baked goods, or make your own crackers from our recipes

CHICKEN LIVER PÂTÉ
Do not tell your friends and relatives what it is to increase the chances of them loving it.

½ lb. chicken liver, cut into small pieces
1 small onion, finely chopped
2 T. organic butter
4 T. flax seed oil
1 t. dry mustard ⎤
¼ t. thyme │
¼ t. marjoram │ Pulverize to powder
¼ t. oregano │
¼ t. pepper ⎦
salt to taste

- Sauté the onion in butter until soft
- Add the liver and cook gently for 2-3 minutes, stirring occasionally
- At the end of cooking mix in all the spices; no salt is added during cooking
- Transfer to a blender, add the oil and salt; process until smooth
- Preferably, serve while warm

Tip: If you're sensitive to garlic, experiment with herbs and spices instead and skip the garlic. Remember, sometimes less is more.

Hint: If using a blender, liquid ingredients should be added first. To ensure a thick enough consistency, reserve some of the liquid ingredients. Add gradually if a thinner dip is wanted.

SPINACH LEGUME SPREAD
½ c. dry beans, lentils or peas
¼ t. cumin
¼ t. pepper
1 t. or more of butter
1 or 2 cloves of garlic, minced
2 c. fresh, chopped spinach
salt to taste
2 t. parsley
Optional: 1 small onion or
2 shallots, minced

- Cook the dry beans as described in our *Beans Crash Course*
- Add cumin and pepper during the last 10 to 15 minutes of cooking
- Melt butter in a pan
- Sauté garlic and onion in butter
- Add spinach and salt, stir and briefly cook until spinach is soft
- Stir in beans while they are still warm
- Add more cumin and pepper to taste
- Continue cooking for an additional 2 to 3 minutes
- Mash the mixture

Consistency choices:

- For a thick, side-dish consistency, return the mashed mixture to the stove and cook longer to evaporate excess liquid
- To thin the mashed mixture, add a bit of leftover bean water or broth and stir to incorporate

Serve as a side dish, a spread on crackers or non-sweet pancakes, a topping for grains, or a vegetable or bean dip

WHEAT-FREE SANDWICH FILLINGS
Use with wheat-free bread, pancakes, tortillas or wraps. Below are a few ideas for hot sandwiches, but the combinations are endless.

STIR-CRAZY CHICKEN
Stir-fry the following:
½ c. chopped chicken
1 T. diced onion
1 clove garlic
¼ c. torn spinach or beet leaves
Salt and curry powder to taste

- Stir-fry onion, garlic and chicken until no longer pink
- Remove from pan
- Add spinach or beet leaves and stir-fry until wilted
- Combine all ingredients and fill sandwich

NUTTY BEEF
½ c. cooked and sliced beef (or more if desired)
2 or 3 steamed asparagus tips, whole
Small dollop of horseradish
6 whole almonds, or 1 T. slivered almonds, or almond butter

BORN-AGAIN TURKEY
⅛ c. chopped dates
½ c. cooked, diced turkey
⅛ c. homemade cranberry sauce

- Mix together before filling sandwich

VEGGIE DELIGHT
½ c. cooked spinach (salt during cooking)

- Squeeze moisture from spinach
- Toss with ½ t. balsamic vinegar and fresh ground pepper
- Arrange mixture on slice of wheat-free bread, pancake or tortilla, and top with ¼ c. grated almond cheese, or your favorite bean spread

Optional: Add cooked egg (boiled and sliced, poached or scrambled)

SAUCES AND PISTOU

20

UN-TOMATO RED SAUCE
*It may not taste exactly like tomatoes, but it provides a bouquet
of flavours and is much healthier than tomato sauce.*

1 lb. carrots, sliced
1 small beet, sliced
2 onions, chopped
2 to 4 cloves garlic
1 bay leaf
2 T. miso (omit if sensitive to)
1 ½ to 2 c. water
1 zucchini, sliced
½ t. ground ginger (optional)
Basil and oregano, to taste
1 T. tamari
1 t. salt
1 T. lemon juice or apple
cider vinegar
2 T. arrowroot
1 c. water

Pressure cooker method:

- Add first 7 ingredients to
  pressure cooker (save
  ½ onion and 2 cloves of
  garlic for sautéing with the zucchini)
- Cook 15 minutes at pressure. Vegetables must be very tender
  - If cooking without a pressure cooker, cook covered in a regu-
    lar pot or a steamer for 30 to 40 minutes
- Remove the bay leaf, transfer mixture to food processor or
  blender and add basil and oregano
- Purée mixture and return to cooker, but do not cover or use
  pressure for remainder of recipe
- Sauté zucchini with the raw onion and garlic in a skillet or a
  pan with butter
- Add tamari, salt, ginger and lemon juice or vinegar
- Combine together all the ingredients in pot
- Dissolve arrowroot in 1 c. cool water and add to mixture in pot
- Stir and cook until thickened, then remove from heat and
  serve as you would tomato sauce over rice or grains

CHILI FROM UN-TOMATO RED SAUCE
Some say this is better than Un-tomato Red Sauce alone.

1⅓ c. beans of your choice (try a blend of ½ c. black, ½ c.
Romano, ⅓ navy)
½ c. sliced celery (or more to taste)
½ lb. ground beef, pork, or lamb
Optional: 1 medium onion, diced
¼ c. chili powder (or more to taste)

- Cook the beans in a pressure cooker for 10 to 20 minutes
- Open cooker, discard the water, replace with fresh water
  and bring to boil
- Follow the preceding recipe for Un-tomato Red Sauce
  with the following additions:
  - sautéed celery with the zucchini, onion and garlic
  - add ground meat(s) of your choice and cook until no
    longer pink
  - sprinkle in chili powder to taste

**RACHAEL, ONE OF
THE CONTRIBUTORS,
ALSO ADDS**
*2 T. olive oil
1 t. mustard, dry*

*She adds these ingredients
just before blending, when
adding the basil
and oregano.*

*To taste: paprika and chili
pepper, powdered hot
sauce and lemon (omit or
use with caution if you are
very sensitive).*

Variations:

Almost anything will work in this recipe. Try with split mung dhal, brown basmati rice and chicken. Add rosemary and cumin. You can also try increasing the amounts of each seasoning for a little extra kick.

VEGETABLES IN LENTILS, DHAL OR SPLIT PEA SAUCE

Don't be intimidated by the length of this recipe, and don't worry if you do not have all the ingredients. Throw in most of the listed stuff and it will work anyway.

½ c. dry legumes (lentils, dhal or split peas)
1 to 2 t. butter
1 to 3 cloves garlic, minced
1 to 2 medium onions, chopped
½ t. finely chopped ginger root
¼ t. curry or turmeric powder
¼ t. coriander powder
¼ t. salt, or to taste

Optional spices/herbs:

¼ t. cumin powder
pinch of red pepper (cayenne or paprika), or to taste
pinch of black pepper, or to taste
pinch of sea vegetables

2 to 3 c. vegetables of your choice (amount depends on your appetite or the number of people being served); examples of appropriate veggies: cauliflower, broccoli, radishes or daikon, green onions, leeks, bok choy, rutabaga, squash, jicama, zucchini

• Wash and soak the legumes for several hours or overnight
• Cook the legumes until half done
• Drain legumes well and set aside
• Use a deep frying pan or a pot with a thicker bottom
• Melt butter in pan
• Sauté the onion and garlic for 2 to 3 minutes at medium heat
• Add ginger and all the desired seasonings
• Keep sautéing and stirring until the seasonings are absorbed
• Stir in the drained legumes
• Cover with two times as much water and bring to a boil
• Reduce the heat and keep simmering until the legumes are very soft or dissolved; mash them if required
• Steam, boil or stir-fry the vegetables until crisp-tender; cook them to a softer texture for those with weaker digestion
• Add salt to bring up the sweetness of vegetables

Serve vegetables mixed with the sauce, or serve separately. Accompany with grains and protein for a complete meal. For example, serve with organic sausage and rice.

FRENCH PISTOU

Jazz up your cooked veggies with this elegant basil sauce.

2 c. fresh basil leaves, loosely packed
⅔ c. chopped parsley
¼ c. pine nuts
⅔ c. olive oil
4 garlic cloves, minced
⅔ c. almond cheese or other alternative
2 T. butter, if desired

- Place all ingredients except the cheese alternative and butter in a food processor or blender and process until smooth
- Add cheese alternative and butter (if using), then process again until thoroughly blended

SASKATOON SAUCE

Makes an excellent topping for pancakes, waffles, scones and gingerbread cake.

2 c. saskatoon berries
1 c. water
1 T. rice syrup
1 T. lemon juice
1 T. tapioca flour

- In a medium sauce pan combine saskatoons, rice syrup and water
- Boil for 5 min, mix in tapioca flour and let cook for another 2 minutes
- Add lemon juice and let it cool down until warm
- Serve warm over pancakes, cakes, breads, porridges etc.

CRANBERRY JAM-OUT SAUCE

600 g. (1.5 lbs.) whole cranberries, frozen or fresh
1¼ c. water
1½ c. date sugar

Optional:
½ t. ground cloves or pumpkin pie spice
½ c. (2 oz.) toasted pecans

- Use a saucepan large enough for all ingredients
- Combine sugar, spices (if using) and water in the pan
- Boil until sugar dissolves
- Add cranberries and reduce heat to medium
- Cook for approximately 5 minutes, until berries just start to pop open
- Use as is, or purée slightly if smaller berry pieces are preferred
- Stir in pecans, if using
- Use while warm, or refrigerate/freeze portions into jars

Note:

Although this is a reasonably healthy take on cranberry sauce, it can also be used as a delicious rice-cream topping or replacement for commercial jams and syrups (if you can't stay away from them).

PLEASE EAT ONLY AS AN OCCASIONAL TREAT. AVOID ALTOGETHER IF YOU TEND TO BE HYPOGLYCEMIC.

CRASH COURSE IN EGG PREPARATION AND EGGS

21

STUFFED EGGS
Impress your friends with this elegant presentation.

3 eggs
2 t. mayonnaise
1 pearl onion or ½ of a small onion, steamed and finely chopped (can be raw onion for the less sensitive)

Optional ingredients:
½ t. finely chopped chives
½ t. finely chopped parsley
pepper and salt to taste
¼ t. mustard seed, finely ground (delete if sensitive)

- Hard boil the eggs:
  - Method 1: start them in cold water and boil for 8 minutes from the start of boiling
  - Method 2: carefully place eggs into boiling water and boil for 10 to 12 minutes
- Either peel the eggs or cut them in half
- If you have peeled the eggs, you may cut the bottoms of the eggs off so they won't tip on the serving plate (use the cut off pieces in the mixture)
- If you left the eggs in the shell and do not have egg cups, stabilize the egg halves with ¼ inch thick slice of cucumber from which you have cut most of the white flesh out. Place the egg onto this hollowed out cucumber slice
- Scoop the yolks out and mix with other ingredients
- Place mixture back into each egg half
- Garnish with anything green and serve

CRASH COURSE IN EGG PREPARATION
- *To prevent breaking the shell during cooking:*
  - *add a bit of salt to the water*
  - *punch a pinhole into the flatter end of the egg with a pin*
  - *if the eggs are cold, warm them up slowly*
- *To expedite peeling, submerge the eggs in cold water for 10 seconds immediately after cooking*
- *To distinguish which egg is cooked and which is not, spin them on their sides. Cooked eggs will spin very fast with no wobble*
- *Both the yolk and the white should be cooked*
- *If you dislike peeling eggs, cut them in half and scoop the egg from the shell with a teaspoon*

Stuffed eggs are best for those who can tolerate cold food. Otherwise, consume it with something warm, e.g. drink warm tea.

FOR EGG SPREADS, PLEASE REFER TO THE SPREADS SECTION.

POACHED EGGS
The classic, but more flavourful.

2 to 4 c. water
¼ to ½ c. vinegar
Optional: ¼ t. caraway seeds
2 to 3 eggs
seasonings and salt, to taste

Older eggs tend to disperse when poached – you can lessen this by pushing them together with a fork.

- Use enough water and vinegar (at ratios indicated) to submerge the eggs when broken into the water
- Bring water, vinegar, caraway seeds and a pinch of salt to a boil
- Break each egg and carefully slip them individually into the water; you may find it easier to first break each egg into a cup and then carefully tip the egg into the boiling water
- Turn the heat down and simmer on low heat for 3 to 4 minutes
- Serve with, or as a topping for legumes, peas, lentils, vegetables, or grains
- Garnish, if desired, with piquant vegetables or olives

SCRAMBLED EGGS WITH VEGETABLES
This is an excellent recipe to experiment with different vegetables and spices, so don't be shy.

1 to 2 c. cauliflower
½ c. any green leafy vegetables, chopped
2 to 4 eggs
pepper, paprika and salt to taste
2 t. butter
Optional:
½ c. daikon or radishes
½ c. beet tops

Variation:
Limit vegetables to cauliflower only. You might also want to include a bit of radish/daikon.

- Chop all vegetables
- Steam-cook or boil them; drain
- While the veggies are cooking, break eggs into a mixing bowl and beat them
- Stir in seasonings
- Melt the butter in a frying pan
- Place the vegetables in the pan and pour the beaten eggs over them
- Scramble until eggs are cooked

EGGS IN A GLASS
A variation of stuffed eggs.

2 to 3 eggs
pepper, paprika, and salt to taste

- Boil the eggs:
  - Option 1: Place the whole eggs into cold water and place over high heat; when the water reaches boiling, the eggs are soft boiled and the yolk is liquid
  - Option 2: Place the whole eggs in boiling water and cook for 3 minutes;
- Boil the eggs a minute longer if less liquid yolk is desired
- Cut eggs in half with a sharp, serrated knife
- Scoop contents out of each shell with a spoon; this is much faster than peeling them
- Place eggs in a small bowl, mash with a fork
- Add pepper, paprika and salt to taste and mix well
- Spoon seasoned mixture into attractive presentation glasses (wine glasses look great)
- Garnish with a pinch of fresh, finely chopped chives, parsley, or any kind of radish; if you can't tolerate raw garnishes, steam or sauté them before topping off the eggs

HIGH SPEED VERSION: SCRAMBLED EGGS WITH VEGETABLES
Use the same ingredients as Scrambled Eggs with Vegetables in the previous recipe.

Hint: Increase the amount of butter from 2 t. to 3 t. to facilitate stir-frying.

- Break eggs into a mixing bowl and beat them
- Chop all vegetables
- Add 2 t. butter to frying pan or wok and preheat
- Add vegetables, seasonings and salt
- Stir-fry until almost done, then turn off the heat
- Add 1 t. more butter if required
- Pour the beaten eggs over the stir-fried vegetables
- Scramble until eggs are cooked, increasing the heat if required

VEGETABLE EGG OMELETTE
Use the same ingredients as Scrambled Eggs with Vegetables, previous recipe.

- Blend all the cooked, drained vegetables with beaten eggs and seasonings
- Melt butter in frying pan over medium heat
- Sauté garlic and/or onion in butter
- Pour egg and vegetable mixture into the heated pan, leaving the sautéed onion and garlic in place
- Ensure mixture is evenly distributed over the frying pan surface
- Cover pan and cook until eggs are set
- Fold over or roll up and move to a warm plate

Serve as is, with grains (millet, buckwheat, rice) and/or with bean filling or spread.

SCRAMBLED SPINACH EGGS
A quick, healthy meal for anytime, not just breakfast.

2 to 3 c. chopped spinach or beet tops
1 onion, chopped
2 cloves garlic, chopped
¼ t. pepper or to taste
¼ t. paprika, or to taste
2 to 3 eggs
salt, to taste
Optional: ½ to 1 c. chopped radishes, daikon or turnip
¼ t. caraway seeds in addition to or instead of pepper

- Briefly sauté onion and garlic over medium heat for about one minute
- Add the spices and vegetables while stirring
- Keep cooking uncovered, stirring occasionally, until the vegetables are tender
- In the meantime, beat the eggs
- While stirring the vegtable mixture, pour in the beaten eggs
- Scramble until eggs are cooked
- **Optional:**
  add more seasonings to taste when adding the eggs

Serve alone, or with grains or legumes. This scramble will also work well as a spread with non-wheat bread, crackers or pancakes, or as a filling for baked squash.

PANCAKES, CRÊPES AND CRACKERS

22

HINTS FOR SENSITIVE PATIENTS

- Start with finely ground flour
- Grinding grains, seeds, nuts and spices just before cooking reduces nutritional losses; freshly ground flour from grains has more nutrients and is better tasting than store-bought flour
- If you are highly food-sensitive, keep your grain-based preparations very simple – at least initially; start with one grain only **For example:** when making pancakes, use one type of flour, such as oat flour or buckwheat flour alone; <u>avoid combining two or more flours</u>
- The next time you make the same recipe, try adding an egg or ground seeds (flax or sesame). If you don't have an adverse reaction to this batter, try one additional grain at a time and make note of how you feel in your food diary; refrain from crackers intitially or soak them
- Pancakes are less irritating than crackers made from the same ingredients
- Let batter stand for several minutes, hours or overnight – it helps with digestion

Millet and rye flours can add a bitter taste. Compensate by combining these flours with tapioca, carob, sorghum or nut flours. You can also add nut milks and spices like cinnamon, cardamom and allspice to avoid increasing the amount of sugar. Or, take advantage of the natural bitterness and work with it by choosing complementary seasonings.

As your health and digestion improve you may start combining flours from different grains to create your own pancake mixtures. This allows you to achieve a variety of tastes and textures that are superior to those experienced with single-grain pancakes.

Note:

Keep in mind that we can adversely react to a combination of grains that we tolerate individually.

Ideally, flour should be ground in a stone grain-grinder. However, even flour made in a coffee grinder is a step up from store-bought flour. Buckwheat, millet, oats, quinoa, amaranth and teff are easy to grind.

WHY SOAK FLOUR?

Soaking improves digestibility and makes the grain or flour softer on the digestive system. This is more important for those with weak and irritated digestive systems.

Soak the flour for several minutes or overnight if possible, stirring occasionally. Flour from harder grains requires longer soaking.

Use just enough water to provide a pancake batter consistency. Batter should pour nicely. The longer the soaking, the more water will be absorbed and required. When the saturation point is reached, the water starts to accumulate on the top of the batter. If this happens, just mix it back in. If the batter is too runny, add more flour and adjust the other ingredients accordingly.

Disregard the amount of water indicated in a recipe when using soaked flour. Use just enough water to absorb fully and provide a pancake batter consistency. In addition, thinner pancakes require more water/milk alternatives than thicker pancakes.

IF YOU STILL THINK THERE'S NO GOOD ALTERNATIVE TO TWO SLICES OF BREAD FOR A SANDWICH, GIVE ONE OF THESE RECIPES A TRY. YOU'LL BE CONVERTED.

Tip: *Regardless of the recipe, don't be afraid to add cooked rice or berries and a little cinnamon to your pancakes.*

ALL PANCAKE FLOURS SHOULD BE SOAKED

Soaking softens the grain's fibre and helps the enzymes start the digestive process. It also reduces adverse reactions caused by lectins.

Highly sensitive people might prefer to soak the ground mixtures overnight.

Hint:

- A thin, but not watery batter makes the nicest pancakes. Shoot for a bit more substance than gravy
- If batter is too thick, the pancakes will be thick and might remain raw in the middle
- If you have added too much water, stir well and add a bit more flour, whisking to break lumps

SIMPLE BUCKWHEAT PANCAKES
You can double or triple this recipe as required.

½ c. buckwheat whole grains
1 egg
pinch of salt
½ c. water
For the pan: 2 T. butter, coconut or dairy

- Grind the buckwheat in a coffee grinder and soak for a few minutes or up to overnight; stir occasionally and add more water if required
- Mix in the egg
- Preheat griddle or frying pan and melt butter to coat the cooking surface
- Pour pancakes onto surface and cook on medium heat until the tops appear dry and bubbles form
- Flip cakes and cook to a golden brown

BUCKWHEAT OR OAT FLOUR PANCAKES
1¼ c. buckwheat or oat flour
¼ t. salt
1 T. rice syrup or barley malt (or to taste)
1 c. rice milk
Optional:
  1 egg
  2 t. baking powder
  Handful of blueberries or Saskatoon berries
  For the pan: 2 T. olive oil or butter (coconut or dairy)

- Combine dry ingredients together in one bowl
- Combine all the wet ingredients in a separate bowl
- Add wet ingredients into dry
- Stir, until lumps are gone
- Preheat griddle or frying pan and add oil or melt butter to coat the cooking surface
- Pour pancakes onto surface and cook on medium heat until the tops appear dry and bubbles form; if not using baking powder, the pancakes will not rise
- Flip cakes and cook to a golden brown

BUCKWHEAT AND QUINOA PANCAKES

1½ c. buckwheat flour
½ c. quinoa flakes or quinoa flour (sorghum can be used instead of quinoa)
2 to 3 T. flax seeds (omit for a crisper version)
1 to 2 eggs
1 to 2 T. oil

Optional:
pinch of salt
for a sweet version, add 1 to 3 T. rice syrup or barley malt
milk alternative

For the pan: 1 to 2 t. butter

- Grind the buckwheat, quinoa and flax seeds in a grinder (a clean coffee grinder works well)
- Soak this mixture for several minutes or longer; add more water if required
- Add the syrup or malt water mixture to the egg bowl
- Add oil, salt and soaked mixture
- Stir ingredients and add more water or milk alternative gradually, stirring to incorporate, until batter can be poured smoothly
- Melt the butter in a frying pan or on a griddle and distribute evenly
- Pour the batter onto the preheated surface in small pancakes
- Fry at medium heat until the surface is well-bubbled
- Check that the underside is golden-brown before flipping

SWEET RICE FLOUR PANCAKES

Naturally sweet pancakes kids will love and easy to make.

1 c. almond milk
1 large egg
½ c. sweet rice flour
⅓ c. oat flour
⅛ to ¼ t. cinnamon
2 T. butter for frying

- In a bowl, blend all the ingredients together
- Melt the butter and fry pancakes to a golden brown

Hint: Stir just enough warm water into rice syrup or barley malt to reduce its stickiness and facilitate blending with other ingredients.

SIMPLE RICE FLOUR PANCAKES

½ c. rice flour
½ c. alternative milk
1 egg beaten lightly
1 t. olive oil
butter for frying
½ t. baking powder
pinch of salt

- In a bowl, mix all the dry ingredients together
- Blend the egg, olive oil and milk together
- Pour the wet mixture into the dry mixture and blend
- If required, add alternative milk or rice flour to achieve the desired pancake consistency
- Melt the butter and fry pancakes in the pan

Tip: Ideal cooking temperature is reached when a drop of water will bounce on the cooking surface.

SIMPLIFIED OATMEAL AND FLAX SEED PANCAKES
These pancakes can be served with either sweet or savoury foods. Just add seasonings accordingly.

1 to 1½ c. oats (grain, not flakes)
⅓ to ½ c. flax seeds
1 to 2 large eggs
Optional:
   pinch of salt
   2 t. oil of your preference
   seasonings of your choice (either sweet or savoury)
   2 t. butter, for pan

- Grind the oat grains and flax seeds in a grinder
- Mix with enough water or milk alternative to create a medium-thick batter that will pour nicely, a bit thicker than gravy
- Let mixture stand for at least two minutes or longer; add water and stir if required
- Whisk eggs and add to mixture, mixing well to incorporate
- Add optional salt and oil, if using, and stir to incorporate
- Lightly butter a frying pan or griddle and place over medium heat; allow the pan to get hot before pouring the pancakes
- Pour pancakes and cook them until their surface is covered with bubbles, then flip and cook another few minutes until the other side is golden brown

TEFF PANCAKES
1⅓ c. teff flour
¼ t. salt
3 T. oil
2 eggs, beaten
1 c. milk alternative (perhaps a bit more if you let the mixture soak for longer)
oil or butter for the pan
Optional:
   2 t. baking powder (product will be unleavened without it)
   1 c. blended or mashed berries or other fruit (blueberries, blackberries; kiwi, mango, or papaya)

- Soak the teff flour for a few minutes or longer
- Combine all the ingredients together
- Preheat griddle or frying pan, add oil or butter to coat surface
- Pour pancakes onto surface and cook until tops are bubbly
- Flip and brown on other side until golden

Tip:
If you prefer a thinly crusted cake, increase the heat, brown both sides, then reduce the heat to fully cook the inside.

Note:
If very juicy fruits are added, the amount of milk alternative can be reduced.

SIMPLE AMARANTH PANCAKES

1 c. whole amaranth or amaranth flour
1 t. flax, sesame, hemp or other seeds
1 egg
1 to 3 t. organic butter

- Thoroughly grind whole amaranth and flaxseed into fine flour; if starting with flour, finely grind the seeds then combine with the flour
- Soak flour in water to make a dough of pancake consistency
- Let mixture stand for at least two minutes or longer; add more water and stir if required
- Beat egg and add to flour/water mixture
- Melt a small amount of butter in a skillet to coat thinly
- Pour the batter in serving-size pancakes
- Cook on both sides until done
- Use higher heat for a crunchier crust and lower heat for a softer crust
- Use higher heat initially to form a crust, then reduce heat to cook pancakes throughout

AMARANTH PANCAKES TAKE LONGER TO COOK THAN THEIR NON-WHEAT COUNTERPARTS.

SORGHUM PANCAKES

2 c. sorghum flour
2 c. water or milk alternative (or their combination)
3 eggs
1 T. oil
½ to ¾ t. salt
2 t. organic butter
Optional:
1 T. sorghum molasses or rice syrup
3 T. baking powder (optional)

- Use sorghum flour or grind whole sorghum into fine flour
- Soak the flour in water to make a batter of pancake consistency; soaking is not required but improves digestibility
- Let stand for at least a few minute up to overnight (optional)
- Beat the eggs and blend them together with oil and molasses/syrup into the flour/water mixture
- Melt a small amount of butter in skillet to coat thinly
- Pour the batter in serving-size pancakes
- Cook both sides until done

PARSNIP AND CARROT PANCAKES
2 carrots medium size
5 parsnips small
¼ c. buckwheat or oat or barley flour
2 eggs
1 t. chives or scallion chopped
1 t. parsley chopped
salt and pepper ground to taste
2 to 3 t. organic butter

- Combine eggs with chives, parsley, salt and pepper
- Grate carrots with the parsnips and mix with the flour and egg mixture
- Mix well, add water or flour if required to achieve a pancake consistency
- Preheat griddle or frying pan and melt butter to coat the cooking surface
- Pour the batter in the pan and cook on medium heat until bubbles start to form
- Flip cakes and cook to a golden brown
- Serve with sweet or savory foods, preferably proteins, for a more complete meal

BUCKWHEAT BARLEY PANCAKES/WRAPS
1 c. buckwheat flour
⅓ c. barley flour
1½ c. water or vegetable broth
2 t. butter or more, for pan
Optional ingredients:
3 T. ground flax or other seeds
2 eggs, beaten; or an additional ⅓ cup of liquid
3 T. oil

- Combine the flour and ground seeds in a mixing bowl
- Add water and whisk

Optional:
let mixture ferment in a warm place overnight to make the pancakes more digestible and fluffier;
otherwise, add water and soak the mixture for at least a few minutes
- Stir in the beaten egg, if using, or use the additional liquid and oil option
- Preheat griddle or cast iron pan
- Add butter or oil and tilt to cover the cooking surface
- When cooking surface is at an even, medium-heat, a drop of water will bounce on the surface
- **For pancakes:** pour the mixture in medium sized cakes that ideally do not touch each other
- **For wraps:** distribute batter thinly in pan
- Cook until the tops are well bubbled (peek underneath to check for level of browning)
- Flip over and brown other side until golden

To serve:

- Wrap vegetables and/or beans inside with a sprinkle of roasted nuts and seeds
- Spread each pancake with bean, seed or nut spreads and roll up like a jelly roll
- For a sweet variation, spread sliced or mashed baked squash over pancake, then sprinkle with roasted nuts and seeds

MEAT OR VEGGIE RICE PANCAKES
2 c. rice flour
¼ c. lentil or small dhal flour
Option: soak for a few minutes to a number of hours (longer is preferable)
1½ c. water
¼ t. salt

½ lb. beef or other meat, minced
2 to 4 t. butter
¼ t. ground pepper
¼ t. powdered ginger
¼ t. cumin powder
¼ t. cinnamon
¼ t. salt, or to taste
1 to 2 cloves garlic, minced

1 c. chopped spinach leaves or a combination of green leafy vegetables: kale, beet tops, chard, dandelions
⅓ c. grated radishes, turnip or daikon

Vegetarian Version

Replace the meat with:

1 c. vegetables
½ c. fresh string beans or fresh green peas
⅓ c. cooked dry beans, lentils, dhal or peas
¼ to ½ c. nuts and seeds

Proceed as in the meat version, except:
- Start stir-frying with nuts and seeds and continue with vegetables and fresh legumes
- Next, add salt and other seasonings
- If using the cooked dry legumes, stir them into the cooked vegetable stir-fry just before topping the pancake

- Combine flours and salt in a bowl
- While stirring, gradually add 1½ c. water and stir until smooth and set aside
- Combine seasonings and work into the minced meat
- Preheat frying pan and melt the butter
- Stir-fry the meat briefly (1 minute)
- Add vegetables and stir-fry an additional minute
- Remove the meat and vegetables
- Into the same pan, add more butter if required and pour the batter so the pancake is the full size of the pan
- Cover and cook for 2 minutes
- Place the cooked meat and vegetable mixture on top of the pancake
- Cover and continue cooking for a few more minutes at low heat until the pancake is done

VARIATIONS:
The pancake can be served on its own, with or without toppings. It can also be made without lentils – just use less water.

The minced meat with vegetables also can be served with meal items other than the pancake.

Hint: Pancakes make great sandwiches or wraps.

BEST EVER PANCAKES OR CRÊPES

These taste so much better than the standard fare and are so simple, you'll wonder why you ever bothered with that packaged stuff!

1 c. rolled oats
½ c. buckwheat flour
Optional: 1 t. baking powder (home-made, ideally)
1 T. ground flax, hemp, sesame or pumpkin seeds
pinch of salt
1 T. rice syrup
1 t. olive oil
Optional: 1 egg
Enough water to soak the grains and to achieve an appropriate batter consistency

* Mix the rolled oats and buckwheat flour and soak the mixture in water or milk alternative for at least a few minutes, stirring occasionally. Soaking it overnight improves its digestibility; use just enough water to absorb fully and provide a pancake batter consistency
* Place the mixture in a food processor or blender and process
* Add the remaining ingredients and blend until thoroughly mixed, stopping to scrape the sides and lid
* Very lightly oil a frying pan and place over medium heat; allow the pan to get hot before pouring the pancakes
* Cook them until their surface is covered with bubbles, then flip and cook another few minutes until the other side is golden brown
* Serve with cooked fruit, butter and rice syrup or barley malt

SQUASH AND SEED CRÊPES

A must-try recipe for great flavour.

1 c. oatmeal flour, rice flour, or 1½ c. rolled oats (slow cooking variety)
1 c. squash, finely diced raw
(try acorn, buttercup, or squash)
¼ c. sesame seeds or other seeds
¼ c. ground pumpkin seeds
pinch of salt
2 to 3 t. butter
water or milk alternative to soak the grains and to achieve an appropriate batter consistency
Optional ingredients:
  1 egg
  1 T. coconut oil or butter
For sweeter pancakes, add:
¼ t. cinnamon, cloves, cardamom
Note: some of us react to cardamom

* Grind oatmeal grains in grinder
* Soak this flour for at least a few minutes, stirring occasionally. Soaking it overnight improves its digestibility; use just enough water to absorb fully, for every ⅓ cup of rolled oats use ⅔ cup of water
* Except for butter, blend all ingredients in a blender with about a cup of milk alternative or water. Add liquid slowly until you achieve a pancake batter consistency; batter should pour nicely
* Preheat frying pan and melt butter at medium heat
* Pour pancakes in desired serving sizes
* Fry to a golden brown on both sides
  * Use lower heat for softer, more consistently cooked pancakes
  * Use higher heat for a thinly crusted cake, but then reduce heat to low to finish cooking the insides

Note:

These pancakes taste great without any additional toppings. If you must have a sweeter taste, top with rice syrup or barley malt, or cooked fruits/berries of your choice. Serve with a glass of almond or cashew milk for enhanced nutrition.

OAT CRACKERS
Served with nut butter or other protein spreads, these are ideal for a fast breakfast or snack.

1 c. oat flour
¼ c. medium size oat flakes
½ t. salt
2 T. butter
⅔ c. water
Optional: pinch of baking soda

- Preheat oven to 300°F
- In a bowl mix oat flour, oat flakes, salt and baking soda
- In a small saucepan, add butter and water and bring to a boil
- Add the oat mixture and turn off heat
- Mix to a moist dough
- Turn dough onto an oatmeal-sprinkled surface and knead until a smooth ball can be formed
- Invert a large baking sheet (to allow you to use the rolling pin on the sheet without hitting its sides)
- Grease the sheet, then sprinkle lightly with oatmeal
- Pat down dough ball, sprinkle lightly with oatmeal and roll out to a 10 inch round
- Cut the round into eight 'pie-pieces' and ease them apart slightly to crisp
- Bake for about 60 minutes until crisp, taking care not to burn the crackers
- Remove from oven, but leave to cool on the baking sheet
- When cool, remove the crackers with a thin metal utensil

NOTE FOR CRACKERS:
The simplest and the most versatile approach to start making crackers is to:

- *use our existing pancake recipes*
- *cook the pancakes longer to desiccate them*

Tips: *Those with very weak digestion should not use the oat flakes.*

Oat grain is very easy to grind in a coffee grinder.

23

GRINGO'S OAT, BUCKWHEAT, RICE OR BARLEY TORTILLAS

Real tortillas require a bit of practice and willingness to get your hands in the flour. Let's make them the non-traditional way: quick, easy and clean.

1 c. flour: oat, buckwheat, rice or barley
use slow-cooking rolled oats (roughly ground)
Optional unless using rice flour:
1 egg or 3 T. ground flax, sesame or hemp seed
1 t. sea salt or pickling salt
1 egg
1 to 2 t. organic butter or coconut oil
2 to 3 c. water or milk alternative

TORTILLA-MAKING IS AN ART – THE MORE TORTILLAS YOU MAKE, THE BETTER THEY GET!

- Grind the whole oat grains into the desired flour texture
- If using rolled oats, leave some whole for texture
- Soak in water in a mixing bowl for at least a few minutes, or overnight
- Use just enough water to fully absorb (⅔ c. water per ⅓ c. oats); longer soaking requires more water
- Combine egg, salt, and water or milk alternative, then stir into dry ingredients; adjust water or the milk alternative to achieve an appropriate consistency
- Preheat frying pan or griddle; brush the surface with butter
- Pour the batter evenly over the surface and use a utensil to create a consistently thin layer
- Cook to a light golden colour before flipping tortilla over to finish cooking

Note: Must add seeds if using rice flour

REAL TORTILLAS MADE FROM OAT, BUCKWHEAT, RICE OR BARLEY
There is no substitute for the real tortilla. The following recipe is our best compromise. One of the advantages is that you can pre-make the dough and keep it in the fridge.

3 c. flour, rice, oat, buckwheat, barley or a mixture of all types (only if not sensitive to multiple grains)
1 t. baking powder
½ t. baking soda
Optional: omit the baking soda and use an additional teaspoon of baking powder
½ to 1 t. sea salt or pickling salt
½ c. organic butter
1 to 1¼ c. warm water

- In a mixing bowl, mix the flour and salt with a fork
- Add butter and cut into the salted flour until the mixture resembles coarse meal with some small pieces intact
- Start adding warm water gradually while kneading until a smooth dough is produced
- Form dough into a ball, leave in the bowl and cover with a damp cloth
- Let stand for 10 to 20 minutes
- Depending on the size of tortillas, divide the dough into 5 to 10 pieces
- Shape each piece into a ball, then flatten between your hands (or use a rolling pin or a clean glass bottle)
  - The desired thickness can be ⅛ to ¼ inch
  - If the dough is sticking to your hands or rolling pin, dust hands, rolling pin and dough with a bit of flour
- Preheat cast iron frying pan (ideal)
  - Some people achieve good results by baking tortillas on a preheated baking sheet
- Cook tortilla without oil on each side (tortillas are done when golden)
- Do not flip the tortilla until the bottom side is golden
  - An occasional small burn spot is an authentic asset, so don't worry; however, do not eat burned tortillas
- Wrap tortillas in a warm, slightly damp towel to keep them warm until served

Note: Traditional recipes use corn or wheat which are not allowed in hypoallergenic diets.

Important:
The weaker the digestion, and the more sensitive the patient, the more finely ground the flour should be, especially for rice or barley.

Hint: If you omit both the baking soda and baking powder, you will create an unleavened tortilla.

THE MOST DIFFICULT PART OF TORTILLA-MAKING IS LEARNING THE APPROPRIATE DOUGH CONSISTENCY.

PIZZA CRUST SIMPLY

Follow the process as below, but bake pizza crust until golden (depending on thickness 20 to 25 minutes).

Top with <u>completely cooked</u> toppings such as:

- Chili from Un-tomato Red Sauce
- Un-tomato Red Sauce with un-cheese or meat
- Variety of stir-fried vegetables and ground meats
- Bean sauce with vegetables

PIZZA CRUST CLASSIC

⅔ c. brown rice flour
½ c tapioca flour or sorghum flour
3 t. xanthan gum
1 T. dry yeast
¼ t. of each marjoram, oregano, basil, sage
½ t. salt
⅔ c. warm water or ⅓ water and ⅓ alternative milk
1 t. olive oil
½ t. vinegar
butter to grease pizza pan

- Preheat the oven to 425° F
- Mix all dry ingredients in a bowl using a wooden spoon
- Make a well in the flour mixture and pour warm water, olive oil and vinegar into it
- Mix well; if the dough is too stiff add 1 T. of warm water at a time and mix it in
- Form a ball and transfer it to a greased 12-inch pizza pan (or a baking sheet)
- Dip your hand in cold water to prevent sticking to the dough and press the dough into the pan forming the pizza shape with a thicker outside rim
- Bake the crust for 10 minutes
- Remove from the oven
- Add toppings to the crust
- Bake for an additional 20 to 25 minutes

Toppings may include:

- Precooked and partially mashed beans
- Lightly stir-fried ground meat and vegetables (zucchini, onions, squash, nuts, seeds and raisins)
- Un-cheese, eggs
- Seeds, chopped nuts or their butters

BREADS

HANDMADE BREAD

OAT, BARLEY AND QUINOA BUNS
This handmade recipe easily becomes the base for bread, buns, muffins, etc. No fancy equipment needed.

1 c. oat flour
¾ c. barley flour
¼ c. quinoa flakes
1 c. tapioca flour
2 t. xanthan gum or ground flax seeds
2 T. rice syrup, barley malt or other natural sweetener
1½ c. lukewarm water
2 T. dry yeast
2 T. melted butter
3 egg whites, slightly beaten
1 t. vinegar
1½ t. salt

- In a large bowl, blend together flours, quinoa flakes, xanthan gum and salt
- In a small bowl, dissolve sweetener in the lukewarm water, then add the yeast
- Mix and set aside until the mixture foams slightly (a few minutes)
- Blend foamed mixture into the dry ingredients
- Add the butter, egg whites and vinegar
- Beat with hand mixer on high speed for 3 minutes; the dough will travel up the beater so hold the mixer on a bit of an angle so the dough will fall off back into the bowl
- Grease a muffin tin with olive oil
- Spoon dough into each cup to about three-quarters full; brush with melted butter; cover the dough and let rise in a warm place until double in bulk (approx 30 minutes)
- Preheat oven to 375°F; older ovens may require 400°F
- Bake for 40 to 45 minutes; when an inserted toothpick comes out clean, the bread is baked
- Remove from pan and place on racks to cool

IMPORTANT: WHAT ABOUT FRENCH TOAST AND OTHER OLD FAVOURITES?
Don't forget: you can still enjoy many old standbys simply by eliminating allergens such as wheat bread, and the 'bad for you' stuff like sugar-laden syrups. So dig out your recipes and make healthy substitutions. You may find yourself cultivating new favourites!

Wheat-free bread does not rise as much as a wheat bread, but it's very satisfying and healthy.

Hint: *If keeping the dough out of drafts is a challenge, try letting it rise in the cold oven with the light on to generate some warmth. Just remember to remove the pan before preheating the oven.*

Quick-rising tip: *Place a pot containing boiling water on the bottom rack of a cold oven and place the dough-filled pan on the rack above it; let stand until it rises.*

HIMALAYAN MILLET AND OAT BREAD

This recipe is an adapted recipe from Hunza Valley near the summit of K2. The bread is traditionally served with apricot spread. If you prefer the original recipe, use two cups of millet and skip the oat. Try both and compare the taste.

1 c. millet
1 c. oat flour
3 eggs
½ c. filtered water
1 ½ t. baking powder
¼ t. salt

- Preheat the oven to 350°F
- Grind the millet in a grain or coffee grinder
- Mix the dry ingredients together
- Beat the eggs well, add water and keep beating them for 2 minutes
- Combine the dry ingredients with the beaten eggs and mix well
- Butter the sides and the bottom of a 5" x 9" loaf pan and dust with a tablespoon of the ground millet
- Pour the batter into the pan
- Bake for 35 minutes or until the inserted toothpick comes out clean

Serve with tea. Spread with butter, nut/seed butter or bean spread.

HIMALAYAN MILLET BREAD WITH PUMPKIN OR SQUASH OR ZUCCHINI OR CARROT

1 c. millet
1 ½ t. baking powder
¼ t. salt
½ t. ground cloves
½ t. ground allspice
1 t. cinnamon
3 eggs
⅛ c. filtered water
1 c. of cooked and mashed pumpkin or squash or 1 c. of raw grated zucchini or carrot (tightly packed)

- Preheat the oven to 350°F
- Grind the millet in a grain or coffee grinder
- Mix the dry ingredients together
- Beat the eggs well, add water and keep beating them for 2 minutes
- Combine the dry ingredients with the beaten eggs and pumpkin or zucchini, mix well
- Butter the sides and the bottom of a 5" x 9" loaf pan and dust with a T. of the ground millet
- Pour the batter into the pan
- Bake for 50 minutes or until the inserted toothpick comes out clean

Serve with tea as is, or spread with butter, nut/ seed butter or bean spread...

Hint: *This is a perfect recipe for making use of your Halloween pumpkin. Cut it up into large chunks and cook in a large pot of filtered water until soft. Scrape the pumpkin off the peel and mash.*

ONE-PAN TEFF FLATBREAD

Teff is an African cereal grain.

1 c. teff
2 c. flour, either barley or buckwheat, or other non-wheat flour
4 c. water
1 medium onion, finely minced
2 cloves garlic, chopped and crushed
¼ t. oregano or marjoram
¼ t. parsley
¼ t. rosemary
¼ t. salt
1 T. organic butter

- Wash and drain the teff
- Boil water in a thick-bottomed casserole or pan suitable for cooking the flatbread on the stovetop
- Add teff and salt
- Reduce heat and stir occasionally, simmering for 10 to 15 minutes until water is absorbed
- Combine flour, garlic, onion and seasonings, then add to cooked teff in the pan
- Gradually add water, stirring to incorporate, and continue stirring until the mixture becomes the texture of dough
- Briefly remove the dough from the pan
- Lightly butter the pan, then pat dough down into the pan, covering the bottom evenly
- Over medium heat, fry the bread on each side until done

Note:

If you have never baked with quinoa before, you may be surprised by its smell when mixing it. However, when it is done, quinoa has a pleasant, mild flavour.

QUINOA RICE BREAD

¼ c. raw unprocessed rice, over-cooked to a mush, cooled and pressed through a sieve (metal mesh strainer)
2 c. ground quinoa or ground amaranth
2½ t. baking powder
1⅓ to 1½ c. milk alternative
3 eggs, beaten
1 t. salt
1 to 2 T. organic butter, melted

- In a small bowl, beat the eggs
- While mixing, gradually pour the milk alternative into the beaten eggs
- In another bowl, combine salt, baking powder and quinoa or amaranth
- Add the liquid mixture (milk alternative and eggs) to the dry mixture and beat well
- Add melted butter and rice; beat well until very light in texture
- Lightly butter the bottom and sides of a shallow, round or square 8-inch baking pan, and dust with flour, tapping out excess
- Turn the mixture into the pan
- Bake in a preheated 400°F oven for 50 minutes, or until a toothpick inserted in the center comes out clean
- Serve hot, with butter

DO NOT BE DISCOURAGED BY THE LENGTH OF THIS RECIPE. IT IS QUITE SIMPLE TO MAKE AND CERTAINLY WORTH THE EFFORT.

Note:

White rice flour lends a more French 'baguette' appearance and taste but it's less nutritious. Brown rice provides a unique texture and more nutrition.

There is a special way to mix the bread dough by hand. While mixing, lift the dough to allow it to breathe. If the dough is sticky, sprinkle and mix in a few tablespoons of rice flour towards the end.

This recipe requires perforated French bread shaped baguette pans for the dough. These are available at specialty culinary stores. If you can't find one, use a 5"x 9" loaf pan. The bread becomes heavier than the typical baguette, but tastes much the same as this French classic.

RICE FRENCH BAGUETTES

No more guilty feelings or adverse reactions after gorging on (or should we say 'cheating with') white French bread. This version tastes better, yet is nutritious and hypoallergenic.

1½ c. white rice flour or 2 c. brown rice flour.
½ c. sweet brown or white rice flour
3 t. xanthan gum
1½ t. salt
2 T. berry or date sugar or honey or rice syrup
1 c. lukewarm water
2 T. yeast
2 T. melted butter, or oil/butter blend
2 eggs
2 t. vinegar
Additional 1 to 2 T. melted butter or coconut oil/butter for greasing the pans and brushing overtop the loaves

- In a bowl, blend flours, xanthan gum and salt
- Dissolve rice syrup or honey in the water, then add the yeast
- Let stand undisturbed until the mixture foams slightly (about 10 minutes)
- Pour the mixture into the dry ingredients
- Add the eggs, butter or oil, and vinegar
- Beat on high speed with an electric mixer for 3 minutes or mix with wooden spoon until the dough forms a ball and does not stick to the bowl
- Dip a knife in cold water and divide the dough in halves
- Dip your hand in cold water and shape each half into a long cylinder
- Place the dough in the buttered baquette pans (or a 5" x 9" loaf pan)
- Dip a sharp knife in cold water and make shallow diagonal slashes every 1½ to 2 inches across the loaves
- Brush the loaves with melted butter
- Cover with a clean cloth and let rise in a warm place until doubled in size (20 to 30 minutes)
- Preheat oven to 350°F
- Brush loaves carefully with melted butter for the second time
- If using the perforated French pans bake for 30 minutes
  If using ordinary loaf pans bake for 40 to 45 minutes
- In either case, a wooden tooth pick should come out clean
- Remove from pan to cool
- Brush again with butter if desired or opt for a high quality flaxseed oil

DARK RYE BREAD

4 c. rye flour
2 c. buckwheat flour
1 c. barley flour
1 t. salt, or more to taste
3 T. active dry yeast
3 to 3¾ c. warm water if adding vegetables
or 2 c. warm water and 1¾ c. warm
alternative milk
⅓ c. molasses (to activate the yeast) or
more to taste

Optional:
   ½ c. grated daikon, rutabaga or kohlrabi
   ¼ t. powdered caraway seeds
   or 1 t. whole caraway seeds for those with
   stronger digestion
   ¼ c. organic butter, melted, or more to taste

LIGHT RYE BREAD

Light refers to the colour of the final product. The light rye bread has the same heavy and nutritious appeal as the dark one.

7 c. light rye flour
3 T. active dry yeast
3½ c. warm water if adding
vegetables
or 2 c. warm water and 1½ c. warm
alternative milk

- Procedure is the same as for Dark Rye Bread

- Dissolve the molasses in warm water, then add the yeast
- Let stand undisturbed until the mixture foams slightly (about 10 minutes)
- Combine all flours, salt, caraway seeds, melted butter, grated daikon in a mixing bowl and mix (reserve a few caraway seeds to sprinkle on the top before baking)
- Add the water/yeast mixture
- While mixing, lift the dough with a wooden spoon to introduce air into it
- If the dough sticks to the bowl, add a bit more flour and continue kneading. Total kneading time should be less than 10 minutes – do not over-knead!
- Cover the dough with a clean cloth and let it rise at a warm, stable temperature until it doubles in size, up to 1 hour
- Tap/punch the dough down
- Melt the butter and butter three 5" x 9" bread pans
- Divide dough into thirds and place in the pans
- Cover the dough with a clean cloth and let rise until double (1 to 2 hours)
- Preheat oven to 375°F
- Brush remaining butter overtop of the loaves, then sprinkle with a few caraway seeds or caraway powder
- Wet a knife and make a shallow diagonal slit on the top of the loaf with a sharp knife
- Bake for 55 to 60 minutes at 375°F

Classic crust tip:
Brush each loaf with salted water two times during the baking. This will give the bread a nice crust.

TRADITIONAL FLAVOUR CAN BE OBTAINED BY:

- *Using a wooden bowl for mixing the dough*

- *Not washing the bowl afterwards; just scraping it out and letting it dry. When making the next batch of dough, the moisture will reactivate the bacteria and give the bread that "Old-World, European flavour".*

SOUR DOUGH STARTER

1 c. rye flour
½ c. water, lukewarm
½ T. dry yeast soaked in

- Mix all ingredients together and cover
- Let sit undisturbed at room temperature for 2 to 3 days
- Use in the following recipe

IMPORTANT:
SKIP THIS RECIPE IF YOU ARE AVOIDING YEAST.

Note:
The barley does not rise as much as wheat does. If using bean flower the dough will rise even less than with barley alone. The resulting bread will be heavier than wheat bread.

SOUR RYE BREAD – OLD FASHIONED
This recipes takes longer to complete since sour dough starter is slower rising than yeast.

10 c. rye flour
1½ c. sour dough starter (see the recipe above)
1½ c. vegetable water, tepid (boil root vegetables in water)
½ c. molasses
2 t. caraway seeds
1 T. salt

- Mix rye flour, sour dough starter, molasses, salt and the vegetable water
- Leave undisturbed in warm place for 3 to 4 hours
- The longer the sitting time, the more sour the taste
- Save 1 c. of the dough as a starter for the next time, keep refrigerated
- Add the caraway seeds and knead until the dough is of a consistent texture and does not stick
- Make into two loaves and place on oiled baking sheets
- Leave undisturbed for 3 to 4 hours to rise to about 1⅓ of its initial volume
- Bake at 350° F for 1¼ to 1½ hours
- Brush during baking with salt water to form a nice shiny crust

HIGHLANDER'S BARLEY BREAD (USES YEAST)
2 c. barley flour
⅓ c. green pea or garbanzo bean or other bean flour (or do not use bean/pea flour and increase the amount of barley from 2 c. to 2⅓ c.)
1 c. tepid/warm water
1 T. yeast
1 T. molasses
1 T. oil
1 t. salt
1 to 2 t. butter for the baking sheet

- In a bowl, mix yeast with ½ of molasses and ½ of water
- Let rise in a warm place for 5 minutes
- In a mixing bowel mix 1 c. barley with the remaining water, molasses, salt, ½ of oil and the yeast/molasses mixture
- While kneading with a wooden kneading spoon, gradually add the rest of the barley and pea/bean flour to make a dough

Continued on next page

Continued from previous page

- Continue kneading in a mixing bowl or on the top of a floured kneading board until the dough is not sticky
- Divide and make into two loaves and place on a greased baking sheet
- Wet the blade of a knife and slash the top of the bread 3 times diagonally
- Let rise for one hour in a warm place
- Preheat the oven to 350°F
- Spread the rest of the oil on the top of the bread
- Bake for 1 hour at 350°F

BREAD MACHINE FAVOURITES

KIDS' FAVOURITE RICE BREAD
Wee ones love this high-rising loaf. Makes one medium loaf.

2⅓ c. rice or almond milk
2 eggs
2 c. brown rice flour
⅔ c. barley flour or quinoa flour
⅔ c. tapioca starch
⅔ c. tapioca flour
½ c. date sugar
4½ t. xanthan gum
1½ t. salt
4½ t. yeast

> **NO SPECIAL ATTENTION IS NEEDED. JUST PLACE IN THE BREAD MACHINE AS USUAL, ON THE STANDARD CYCLE.**

BREAD MACHINE BARLEY, BUCKWHEAT, RICE BREAD
½ c. brown rice
1½ c. barley flour
1½ c. buckwheat flour
¾ c. water
½ T. active dry yeast
1 t. salt
2 t. rice syrup
1 to 2 t. organic butter

- Precook the brown rice for 30 to 40 minutes in boiling water
- Remove from heat and pour into a 2-cup measuring container
- Add enough warm water to bring the mixture to 1½ cups
- Combine all ingredients, transfer to the bread maker, and use the regular setting

SWEET BREADS

HIMALAYAN MILLET BREAD WITH APRICOTS AND PRUNES

1 c. millet
1 t. baking powder
¼ t. salt
3 eggs
¼ cup filtered water
1 c. finely chopped dried apricots
½ c. nuts or seeds optional

- Preheat the oven to 350°F
- Grind the millet in a grain or coffee grinder
- Mix the dry ingredients together
- Beat the eggs well, add water and keep beating them for 1 minute
- Combine the dry ingredients with the beaten eggs and mix well
- Mix in the chopped apricots and nuts
- Butter the sides and the bottom of a 5" x 9" loaf pan and dust with a tablespoon of the ground millet
- Pour the batter into the pan
- Bake for 35 minutes or until the inserted toothpick comes out clean
- Serve with tea; if not using the nuts/seeds in the bread, use butter or nut/seed butter as a spread

Note:
The batter will appear runny at first. Don't worry about it, the millet will absorb all the fluids.

Variation:
Replace apricots with prunes and add ¼ t. of nutmeg to the dry mixture.

SORGHUM BREAD WITH NUTS/SEEDS AND APRICOTS

2½ c. sorghum
2 c. apricots dried finely chopped
1 c. nuts or seeds chopped or coarsely ground
1⅓ c. milk alternative or water (or their combination)
1 c. rice syrup or barley malt (½ to ¾ c. sorghum syrup)
2 eggs
¼ c. oil
4 t. xanthan gum
1½ t. baking powder
2 t. butter
Optional:
   ½ t. nutmeg
   ½ t. ground cloves
   ½ t. ground allspices

- Preheat the oven to 350°F
- Grind the sorghum in a grain or coffee grinder
- Mix the dry ingredients together
- Beat the eggs well, add water/milk and keep beating them for 1 minute
- Combine the dry ingredients with the beaten eggs and mix well
- Mix in the chopped apricots and nuts
- Butter the sides and the bottoms of two 5" x 9" loaf pans and dust with a tablespoon of the sorghum flour
- Spoon the batter into the pans
- Bake for 55 minutes or until the inserted toothpick comes out clean
- Brush the surface of the loaves with milk alternative or salt water several times during baking to make a shiny crust
- Serve with tea. If not using the nuts/seeds in the bread, use butter or nut/seed butter as a spread

GINGERBREAD CAKE
1 c. molasses
1 c. organic butter
1 c. sour rice milk or other milk alternative (to sour, stir 1 T.
vinegar into 1 c. rice or other milk alternative and let stand for
15 minutes, stirring occasionally)
1 egg
2½ c. buckwheat flour
½ t. ground ginger
½ t. cinnamon
¼ t. nutmeg
½ t. ground cloves
2 t. baking soda
½ t. baking powder

- Preheat oven to 350°F
- In a large bowl, blend together the molasses, butter, milk
  alternative and egg
- In a separate mixing bowl, combine dry ingredients
- In two or three portions, mix dry ingredients into wet, stirring
  after each addition
- Lightly butter and dust a 9" x 13" cake pan with flour
- Transfer the batter to the cake pan and smooth out evenly
- Bake the bread for about 35 minutes
- Cake is done when a toothpick inserted comes out clean
- Serve with sesame seeds or your favourite nut/seed butter

NOTE:
THIS RECIPE WAS
TESTED BY THE
TOUGHEST EXPERTS
UNDER THE AGE
OF TWELVE AND
CONSISTENTLY
PASSED WITH
FLYING COLOURS.

FEEL LIKE A FULL-BLOWN DESSERT INDULGENCE? DON'T DESPAIR, THERE ARE HEALTHY DESSERTS!

TEFF FLAKE COOKIES

1 c. rolled oats
¼ c. uncooked teff (ground for those with weaker digestion)
1 c. non-wheat grain flour (buckwheat, barley)
1 t. baking powder
¼ t. salt
½ c. almond milk or other milk alternative

1 egg, beaten
2 T. organic butter or olive oil (other than flax-seed or canola)
¼ t. almond extract (or more if rice milk is used)
2 t. vanilla
¼ c. rice syrup or ⅓ c. barley malt

- Mix the dry ingredients together in one bowl
- Mix the wet ingredients together in another bowl
- Add the wet ingredients into the dry, and combine with wooden spoon or use an electric mixer until well blended
- If the dough appears excessively runny, let it stand for a few minutes to absorb the excess moisture
- Drop by spoonfuls onto a lightly buttered cookie sheet
- Bake at 350°F for 10 to 12 minutes (depending on your oven); edges will be light brown; do not overcook
- Cool and store in a tightly closed container

HAYSTACKS (REFRIGERATOR COOKIES)
Delicious and addictive.

1 c. rice syrup
6 T. cocoa (if using carob, ensure it does NOT contain corn)
½ c. butter
½ c. rice milk (or other milk alternative)
½ t. vanilla
1 c. shredded coconut
3 c. rolled oats (Hint: wild oats provide the nicest texture)
Optional: grated nuts may be partially or fully substituted for the oats

- Combine cane sugar or rice syrup, cocoa, butter and milk alternative in a saucepan
- Bring to a boil, stirring frequently
- Remove from heat
- Immediately stir in coconut, vanilla, oats and/or nuts
- Cool slightly, then form into small balls or cookies by hand (make them small because they are so sweet)
- Drop onto a greased cookie sheet and refrigerate until firm

TEFF CAROB COOKIES

¾ c. rice flour
1½ t. carob powder
Caution: carob may contain corn
¼ c. rice syrup or other natural sweetener
¼ t. vanilla or almond extract
¼ c. barley flour
¼ c. uncooked teff
½ c. water

Continued on next page

- Mix the dry ingredients together in one bowl
- Mix the wet ingredients together in another bowl
- Add the wet ingredients into the dry, and combine with wooden spoon or use an electric mixer until well blended
- Drop by spoonfuls onto a lightly buttered cookie sheet
- Bake at 350ºF for 10 to 12 minutes (depending on your oven); edges will be light brown; do not overcook
- Cool and store in a tightly closed container

SORGHUM GINGER COOKIES

1 c. sorghum flour
1 c. oat flour
⅓ c. chickpea flour
½ c. butter
1 c. rice syrup or sorghum molasses or barley malt
1 egg
1 t. baking soda
½ t. salt
2 t. ginger
2 t. cinnamon powdered

- In a bowl, cream butter, syrup/molasses and egg until smooth
- Mix all dry ingredients and gradually blend them into the cream mixture
- Cover the dough (with a saran wrap) and chill for 1 hour
- Using a tea spoon for a rough measure, roll dough into small balls, approximately 1 inch in diameter
- Generously butter a baking sheet and place the cookies on it, leaving space between the cookies (the cookies will spread during baking)
- Preheat the oven to 350ºF and bake for 12 minutes or until the edges turn golden in colour
- Let cool off slightly and remove from the sheet

Note: Avoid chickpea or pea flour if you have problems digesting beans and replace with sorghum, rice flour or millet

SORGHUM VANILLA COOKIES

2 c. sorghum flour
¼ c. sweet rice flour
½ c. chickpea or green pea flour
1½ c. sorghum molasses or rice syrup or barley malt
2 eggs
½ to ¾ c. organic butter
2 t. xanthan gum
2 t. cream of tartar
1 t. baking soda
2 t. vanilla (optional, but it dramatically improves the taste)
¼ t. salt

- In a bowl, cream butter, syrup/ molasses and eggs
- Mix all dry ingredients and gradually blend them into the cream mixture
- Chill the dough for 1 hour
- Using a teaspoon, roll dough into small balls (some cooks prefer to shape them into sticks)
- Butter a baking sheet and place the cookies on it, leaving space between cookies (the cookies will spread during baking)
- Preheat the oven to 350ºF and bake for about 12 minutes depending on size
- Remove from the sheet while warm

Tip: When making the Sorghum Ginger Cookie balls, dip your fingers in cold water to prevent the dough from sticking to your fingers. Cooling will make the dough stiffer and more pliable.

MUFFINS

MIXED BERRY MUFFINS

2 c. ground almonds
½ c. sweet rice flour
1 t. baking powder
1 t. xanthan gum
1 c. rice or almond milk
4 eggs
2 T. rice syrup
1 c. melted butter and cooled slightly
1 t. natural vanilla extract
1 T. fresh lemon juice
1 c. frozen berries of choice

- Line medium size muffin pans with muffin cups. Preheat oven to 350°F
- In medium bowl, mix together the wet ingredients
- In a larger bowl, mix together the dry ingredients
- Add the wet mixture to the flour mixture and mix only until combined
- Mix in berries gently
- Spoon the batter into the muffin cups, fill the cups only about ⅔ full
- Bake for 20 to 25 minutes until golden on the surface
- Leave sitting in pans to cool for 15 minutes

Makes 18 medium size muffins

TEFF OAT BRAN MUFFINS

½ c. teff seeds
(lightly grind them
for sensitive digestive systems)
¼ c. boiling water
2 T. oil (not flax oil)
2 c. non-wheat grain flour or a combination of non-wheat grain flours (e.g. 1 c. barley, ¾ c. tapioca, ¼ c. buckwheat)
½ c. rolled oats
1½ t. baking soda
1 egg slightly beaten
½ c. rice syrup or other natural sweetener
1 c. milk alternative
1 T. ground flax seeds or xanthan gum
(skip if sensitive to either one)

- Preheat oven to 375°F
- Place teff in a medium bowl
- Pour boiling water over teff and stir to moisten completely
- Set aside to cool
- In a large bowl, mix flour, oats and baking soda
- When teff is cool, stir in sweetener, oil, milk alternative, egg and flax seeds or xanthan gum
- Add this mixture to the dry ingredients and combine with a few strokes. Not all the dry ingredients will be moistened in the batter
- Fill muffin cups to ¾ full
- Bake for 20 to 30 minutes
- Let cool before removing from tins

IMPORTANT:

Freeze the berries first. If you don't, the berries shrink and leak juice and it makes the muffins soggy.

AMARANTH MUFFINS

1¾ c. amaranth flour
⅔ c. + 2 T. hot water
¼ c. nuts, finely ground
¼ c. arrowroot
¼ c. oil
¼ c. barley malt or rice syrup or sorghum molasses
2 T. vinegar or lemon juice
2 t. baking soda
1 t. cinnamon
1 t. vanilla
pinch of salt
½ c. dry fruits, chopped (optional)
1 egg (optional)

- Line medium size muffin pans with muffin cups. Preheat oven to 375°F
- In medium bowl, mix together the wet ingredients
- In a medium bowl, mix together the dry ingredients
- Add the wet mixture to the flour mixture and mix only until combined
- Mix in berries gently
- Spoon the batter into the muffin cups, fill the cups full
- Bake for 20 to 25 minutes until feels firm
- Leave sitting in pans to cool for 15 minutes

Makes 10 medium-size muffins

MILLET MUFFINS

1-½ c. millet flour
½ c. chicpea flour
1 c. water or milk alternative
¼ c. oil
¼ c. rice syrup or barley malt or sorghum molases
1 T. baking powder
¼ t. cinnamon and/or vanilla
¼ t. salt (optional)

- Line medium size muffin pans with muffin cups. Preheat oven to 350°F
- In medium bowl, mix together the wet ingredients
- In a medium bowl, mix together the dry ingredients
- Add the wet mixture to the flour mixture and mix only until combined
- Mix in berries gently
- Spoon the batter into the muffin cups, fill the cups only about ⅔ full
- Bake for 15 to 20 min. until golden on the surface
- Leave sitting in pans to cool for 15 minutes

Makes 12 medium-size muffins

Note: Avoid chickpea or pea flour if you have problems digesting beans and replace with sorghum, rice flour or millet

Tip: To make a bread instead of Millet Muffins, shape the dough into a loaf and bake for 35 to 40 minutes, or until the tooth pick comes clean.

GRANOLA, CHEWS

Note: *Make the crispy nuts first, or have them on hand. See our Nut and Seed Roasting Crash Course for information.*

NO BAKE COCOA/CAROB CHEWS
A highly satisfying, yet nutritious treat.

1 c. crispy almonds
1 c. crispy cashews or pecans
½ c. cocoa or carob powder (only if it does NOT contain corn)
½ c. brown rice syrup
3 T. butter
1 T. vanilla extract
½ t. sea salt
1 c. dried, unsweetened coconut
(or shredded dry coconut)

- Place almonds and cashews in food processor and pulse until finely chopped but not pulverized
- Place rice syrup, butter, carob powder, vanilla and salt in a glass container
- Set container in simmering water until syrup is melted; mix ingredients well
- Add melted mixture and coconut to nuts in food processor; pulse a few more times
- Line a cookie sheet with buttered parchment paper and press mixture about ½ inch thick (moisten your hands with hot water to prevent the mixture from sticking to your hands or use the back of a spoon)
- Wrap in parchment paper and refrigerate several hours

Cut into small squares and store in an airtight glass container in the refrigerator to reduce destruction of essential fatty acids.

NUTTY GRANOLA
This recipe doubles nicely, just remember to bake it in a higher-sided pan.

4 c. rolled oats (not quick-cooking)
1 c. rice bran or oat bran
½ c. sunflower seeds
½ c. pumpkin seeds
½ c. chopped walnuts
½ c. chopped almonds
½ c. dried cranberries
½ c. dried currants, blueberries or blackberries
1 t. natural vanilla extract
¼ to ⅓ c. organic virgin olive oil
¾ c. or less, rice syrup
salt to taste, if required

- Preheat oven to 250°F
- Place all ingredients except oil and syrup in a bowl large enough to accommodate, and combine manually
- Add oil in two or three pours and stir to distribute evenly
- Pour in maple syrup until mixed well and evenly moistened; mixture will be crumbly and sticky
- Spread mixture on lightly oiled cookie sheet or oblong pan
- Bake for 90 minutes, stirring every 15 minutes until the mixture is golden brown and dry
- Cool thoroughly and store in airtight container. Freeze for maximum preservation, especially if you cannot use the full batch promptly

FRUITS, CRISPS, JAMS, DUMPLINGS AND PIES

FRUIT CRASH COURSE

When eating fruit by itself, slice it and cook it lightly to preserve its natural sweetness and crisp taste. Also, do not eat fruits from a blender, as this may increase fluctuation in blood sugar levels. For those who can't chew well, simply mash the fruit with a fork. Steaming, boiling and stir-frying are usually the fastest and simplest cooking methods. Baking works as well, but takes longer.

Steps to Minimize Nutrient Losses:

* Do not pre-cut and store
* Wash and cut fruit just before cooking (cut and transfer directly to the boiling water or hot oil)
* Submerge fruits in cold water for a few seconds before cleaning
* Use cold water and a natural bristle brush to scrub fruit
* Do not remove the skin if soft – the most nutrient rich part of the fruit is the skin and the part directly under it; this is another reason to buy organic
* Cut fruit into smaller pieces to reduce the cooking time
* For boiling: bring the water to a boil first and boil briefly (to allow some oxygen to escape from the water) then add the fruit
* For stir-frying: heat up the oil, then add the fruit
* Add fruit to recipes during the last minutes of cooking:
  * Harder fruits are added before the softer ones
  * The longer you cook the fruits, the softer they will become and the less irritating
  * The more sensitive and weaker your digestion, the more cooked and soft the fruits must be
* Serve cooked fruit immediately:
  * Letting cooked food sit will progressively reduce its nutrient value
  * 'Sitting time' nutrient loss will exceed any loss which might occur during cooking
* Do not store cooked fruits

Fruits and berries can also be lightly stir-fried with butter. Try with strawberries and add a pinch of cinnamon and freshly ground black pepper.

HOT STRAWBERRIES
This recipe is good for blueberries and other berries as well.

1 c. fresh strawberries
1-2 t. of butter
1 t. berry sugar (optional)
pinch of black pepper
pinch of cinnamon
optional

* Wash, hull and slice fresh strawberries
* Melt the butter in a frying pan
* Add a pinch of ground black pepper
* Sauté the strawberries until they start turning pale colour
* If the strawberries are really tart, add berry sugar as required
* Spoon into small glass dishes and serve warm as a dessert or as a topping for pancakes, crepes, breads, cakes, porridges

PEAR UN-PIE

This tastes like pie filling and is far better for you than the pastried version of this well-loved dessert. An occasional treat for those not sensitive to pears.

3 large pears
⅓ c. rice syrup or barley malt or other approved sweetener (or less to taste)
⅛ c. pure cranberry juice or 1 T. lemon juice
½ t. cinnamon
2 t. butter (optional)

- Preheat oven to 350°F
- Peel and core pears, and slice thinly
- Mix the syrup, cranberry/lemon juice and cinnamon in a bowl large enough to allow you to stir the pear slices in it without any of them escaping over the side
- Add the pear slices and stir to coat well
- Arrange the slices flat in a baking dish large enough to hold them
- If using butter, dot over top the arrangement and sprinkle on a bit more cinnamon if desired
- Bake for 35 minutes, stirring twice within that time

SERVE PEAR UN-PIE ANY TIME OF DAY. TRY IT FOR BREAKFAST WITH A CHEESE SUBSTITUTE FOR PROTEIN. YUM!

Tip: Rachael also fries them after the steaming for better taste and golden crust.

SQUASH AND SESAME SEED DUMPLINGS (SWEET)
Easier to make without brown rice flour.

⅓ c. sesame seeds, ground (soak if desired)
¾ c. squash cooked and mashed
¼ c. finely shredded coconut
¼ t. cinnamon
a pinch of one or all of the following: allspice, cloves, ginger, or cardamom

1½ c. sweet rice flour
Or
1 c. sweet rice flour with ½ c. brown rice flour
½ c. tapioca starch
1 to 2 eggs
1 T. oil
½ to 1 c. water

- Blend the mashed squash, sesame seeds, coconut and spices
- Mixture should be very thick, not runny
- Place rice and tapioca flours in a bowl and mix a slightly beaten egg(s) into the combined flours, if using
- Gradually mix in enough water to form a dough-consistency
- Dust the work surface with rice flour and knead dough to a very pliable texture
- Roll the dough into a 1½" to 2" cylinder diameter and slice into sandwich thickness slices
- Either hand-flatten or roll out to a thickness of about ⅛". (If you do not have a rolling pin, use a clean glass bottle.)
- With a spoon, place some of the squash blend on the flattened dough and wrap dough around filling, sealing the edges. Continue until all "pockets" are filled. ("Perogy" shapes are the easiest.)
- Steam dumplings in a steamer until thoroughly cooked. The surface will appear glazed
- If a sweeter taste is desired, serve with a drizzle of rice syrup or barley malt overtop
- Also delicious served with butter, or a nut/seed butter of your choice.
- Serve with licorice tea or any other sweet tea

RICE AND ALMOND FLOUR PIE CRUST

If you're an inexperienced pastry maker, you'll like this "right in the pie plate" approach. This is a gluten-free dough that will not toughen when handled.

Note: Not suitable if your digestion won't tolerate almonds.

⅓ c. whole almonds
¾ c. brown rice flour
¼ t. ground cinnamon
pinch of ground cloves
3 T. water
2 T. oil
2 to 3 T. rice syrup or barley malt

- Preheat oven to 350°F
- Grind ⅓ cup whole almonds to a fine powder in a blender
- In a 9-inch pie plate, combine the ground almond flour, brown rice flour, cinnamon and cloves
- Mix well with a fork
- Combine the water, oil and rice syrup and heat on low setting until rice syrup liquefies
- Stir the warm liquid, then drizzle it over the flour mixture in the pie plate, stirring with a fork until well blended
- Let stand until the dry ingredients absorb the liquid
- Shape the crust by pressing mixture firmly into place with your fingers, covering bottom and sides of plate evenly
- Bake before or after adding filling
- Bake empty crust until lightly brown (about 5 minutes)
- Yield: one crust

Filling: Use with sweet or savory fillings. Savoury filling ingredients may include vegetables, beans, meats, eggs, nuts and seeds.

Filling may be baked together with a top crust, or made separately and poured hot into the baked pie shell.

THIS RECIPE IS FOR THOSE WHO WON'T GIVE UP THEIR SWEET TOOTH.

RACHAEL'S PECAN PIE
Uses Rice and Almond Flour Pie Crust.

2 eggs
1 to 1½ c. fruit sugar or date sugar
¾ c. rice syrup
1 T. molasses
4 to 5 t. organic butter, melted
1 c. currants or raisins
¾ c. pecans (can be chopped if preferred)
2 t. vinegar
pinch of sea salt
½ t. pure vanilla extract

- Beat eggs well
- Add fruit sugar, rice syrup, melted butter and beat again
- Add the currants/raisins, walnuts, vinegar, salt, vanilla and mix vigorously
- Make the almond and rice flour pie crust, as above
- Put filling in pie filling ¾ full
- Bake at 350°F until golden brown and bubbly on top
- Baking time varies: start checking pie after 20 minutes; may take up to 40 minutes to fully cook in the centre
- Let cool fully before serving

PUMPKIN CUSTARD

1½ c. puréed pumpkin
(not pumpkin pie filling!)
1 c. almond milk
½ c. rice syrup
3 eggs
1 t. cinnamon
½ t. ground ginger
¼ t. ground nutmeg
¼ t. ground cloves
1t. vanilla
pinch of salt

- Lightly butter 6 small dessert-size baking bowls
- In a medium mixing bowl, mix eggs and rice syrup and add puréed pumpkin
- Gradually mix in almond milk
- Mix in the spices and vanilla
- Pour the mixture into the baking bowls
- Place the small bowls in a large shallow baking pan and add water until about 1 inch deep
- Bake at 325°F until custard is set and inserted knife comes out clean, about 1 to 1¼ hours
- Remove the bowls with a spatula; cool before serving
- For presentation, garnish with fresh mint leaves, a few slices of strawberry or other fruit choices like blueberries, raspberries or kiwi

GINGER PEAR CRISP

This is a delicious recipe. Skip the ginger if you suspect an adverse reaction to it.

Filling

1 kg or 2 lbs pears (4 large pears) peeled, cored and sliced
½ c. dried cranberries (optional)
1 T. fresh lemon juice
3 T. pear juice
2 T. tapioca or arrowroot flour
2 t. grated ginger root, or ½ t. dried ginger
2 t. vanilla
2 t. cinnamon
½ t. nutmeg

- Place all ingredients in a bowl and toss

Topping

1¼ c. rolled oats
½ c. oat flour
1 c. pecans, chopped
1 t. cinnamon
1 t. vanilla
½ c. oil or melted butter
¼ to ½ c. brown rice syrup

- Combine all dry ingredients
- Mix together oil/butter, vanilla and rice syrup and pour over the dry ingredients
- Place the fruit filling in a 9" x 13" buttered pan and cover with topping
- Wet your knuckles and press down gently
- Bake at 350°F for approximately 40 minutes
- Let cool for 10 minutes before serving

RED BEET JAM
500 g. red beets (4 medium size red beets)
1¼ c. water
3 T. rice syrup
½ lemon (lemon juice and rind)
½ t. ground cloves
½ t. ground allspice
¼ t. finely grated ginger root or dried ginger powder
½ c. chopped hazelnuts, pecans and/or walnuts
(nuts are optional)

- Peel and coarsely grate the beets and place in a
  medium-size pot
- Add water and bring to a boil, then lower heat and simmer for
  about ½ hour
- Add all spices, rice syrup, lemon juice and rind and simmer for
  another hour
- Cool slightly and purée the mixture in a blender
  (blend in batches)
- Return to the pot, add the nuts (optional) and simmer to
  achieve desired jam consistency
- While hot, ladle into small glass jars, tightly seal with a lid and
  store in the fridge

Makes about 3 jam jars

ORANGE BEET JAM
500 g orange beets (4 medium size beets)
1½ c. water
3 T. rice syrup
½ lemon (lemon juice and rind)
¼ t. ground cloves
¼ t. turmeric
½ t. cinnamon
½ c. sliced almonds, optional

- Same preparation as described above for
  Red Beet Jam.

BONES CRASH COURSE

29

- Trim the meat and external fats off the bone

- Boil enough water to cover the bones; add bones, reduce heat and simmer until the residual meat and external fat (if any) are cooked

- Remove the bones, cut off the residual meat and fat; cover and set aside in a warm place to prevent cooling

- Hit the large, hollow bones against the cutting board to extract the bone marrow; if the bone marrow is not sliding out from the bone, continue cooking for a few more minutes and repeat the process

- Kids love fresh, warm bone marrow with a dash of salt. Marrow mono-unsaturated fats are easy to absorb and are good for them. Start slowly if your child's digestion is very weak; kids also usually like the meat off the still-warm soup bones

- Place the bones, ligaments and tendons back into the soup. Keep simmering for an hour to several hours to attain your preferred softness; eat the softer tendons and ligaments to help support your own ligaments

- Return the meat to the soup a few minutes before the soup is served to prevent overcooking it

- European cooks have a motto: "As soon as you get to work, turn the fire on under the bones"; they used to cook the bones for up to three days, then chopped off the softer parts of the bones, ground them, and added this back to the stock

- Depending on how fatty the meat and bones are, you might need to skim off the surface fat; refrigerate and use it for baking or stir-frying

- Those of us who have problems digesting fats might have to precook the bones in one water, remove the bones and cook them again in fresh water

- Save the original cooking water, separate the fat and use the liquid as stock starter

ABOUT COOKING WITH BONES

Bones provide delicious flavour and superior nutrition. The longer you cook bones, the more minerals and mono-unsaturated fatty acids will be released.

We are primarily interested in the healthy fats from bone marrow because it is those fats that our brain and nervous system are made of.

When cooking bones, start by simmering them, then use the same liquid to cook other ingredients – beans, vegetables, etc.

BONE-BASED SOUP WITH QUINOA, BLACK-EYED PEAS AND KIDNEY
*The ultimate health food that tastes good and does not
leave you hungry.*

⅓ to ½ beef kidney or 1 game kidney cut into bite-size pieces
(verifiably organic source only)
Or: substitute any other meat for the kidney
1 to 2 lbs. beef, bison, pork, lamb or game bones
½ c. dry black-eyed peas or green peas
¾ c. quinoa
¼ t. oregano
¼ t. thyme
½ t. caraway seed
¼ to ⅓ c. usnea – for the adventurous (for a description,
see our herbs and spices section)
½ t. salt, or to taste
½ c. leeks, chopped
½ c. carrots, diced
2 or more cloves garlic, minced
1 to 1½ c. squash, diced (acorn or similar squash)
1 c. any chard leaves, chopped (or other leafy vegetables
such as mustard, kale, beet tops)

- Cut the kidney into smaller pieces and soak in a large amount
  of water. Keep changing the water as often as practical; soaking may be done overnight – just change the water a couple of
  times before retiring
- Wash black-eyed peas and soak for several hours or overnight,
  changing the water as often as practical; see the *Crash Course
  in Beans and Legumes*, for more information
- Start cooking with the bones as described in the *Crash Course
  in Bones*. You can let them cook for several hours
- Drain the black-eyed peas and add to the simmering stock
- Wash the quinoa, drain, and add to the stock about 10 to 15
  minutes after the black-eyed peas; if using usnea, add it at
  this time
- 10 minutes later, add kidneys, squash, leeks, carrots, garlic
  and all seasonings
- Cook uncovered until the peas become softer and the quinoa
  partially dissolves
- Add the leafy vegetables about 5 minutes before the soup
  is done

Serve with or without the bones. This soup provides a
complete meal.

*" Following a diagnosis of
breast cancer a little more
than five years ago, I
became a regular patient
of Dr. Kodet. With the help
of his herbal prescriptions,
dietary remedies and his
general holistic care, I have
maintained a sense of
sound health. I appreciate
his conscientiousness in
determining symptom
source, his physical
assessments, and his
ongoing reassessments
of what approach might
be the most appropriate
for my health going
forward. I have found that
Dr. Kodet's methodology
is not a 'cookie-cutter'
one, but rather, is wholly
individualized according
to the shifts and changes
occurring in my health."*

*– Dr. Nancy Dudley
(Professor, University
of Calgary)*

BONE-BASED BEEF AND BARLEY/RICE SOUP
*The power soup that leaves all the other 'hearty soups'
in the dust.*

1 to 2 lbs beef, bison, pork, lamb or game bones (chicken is also
acceptable)
½ to 1 lb beef of any kind (or other preferred meat), cut into bite-
size pieces
½ c. dry pinto beans, dry green peas, navy beans, Great Northern
beans or adzuki beans
Grain blend of your choice:
⅓ c. barley and ½ to ¾ c. brown rice – use the greater amount
for a thick soup; (use 1c. rice only for those who are sensitive to
barley. If preferred and not sensitive to it, use ¾ to 1 c.
of barley)
½ t. marjoram
¼ t. celery seeds or basil
½ t. caraway seed
¼ t. black pepper
½ t. salt, or to taste
½ c. chopped onions
2 cloves minced garlic (or more if desired)
2 c. vegetables (choose two or more vegetables such as celery,
turnips, parsnips, daikon, broccoli, cabbage, cauliflower, beet
tops, squash, or whatever suits your fancy)

Hints: *Try heart or
any cheaper, leaner cut.
Another option is to use
a more expensive cut,
remove the meat as soon
as it's done, and serve it
as your main course meat.*

*This recipe works well
even without beans
or peas.*

• Please refer to *Crash Course in Bones*, to prepare bones
• Wash beans, barley/rice, and soak each ingredient separately
  for several hours or overnight. Change the water a few times,
  as convenient
• Strain the beans and barley/rice and add to the
  simmering stock
• Add onions and garlic
• Cook until the beans and barley are soft
• Add remaining vegetables with spices and salt
• Cook until done

This soup stands on its own and provides a complete meal.

QUICK VEGETABLE STOCK
Just top up with any certified organic vegetables.

2 c. onions, peeled and coarsely chopped
1½ c. beet tops, chopped
1 c. broccoli, chopped
½ c. rutabaga, chopped
1 medium turnip, cubed
1 bunch of celery tops, chopped
2 whole garlic cloves, peeled
1 bay leaf
1 t. salt (kosher, pickling, or sea salt is best)
2 sticks of dried sea vegetable or ½ t. kelp

- Place all ingredients in a large stock pot and add sufficient filtered water to cover
- Bring to a boil, then reduce heat and simmer for 2 hours
- Strain through a fine sieve or cheesecloth
- Taste and adjust seasonings or salt to your liking

SIMPLE SOUP STOCK
Uncooked chicken bones (1 to 2 lbs)
1 carrot
1 small onion
1 celery stalk
1 T. basil dry
4 cloves garlic
salt and pepper to taste

- In a large pot, simmer the bones for one hour
- Remove the bones and chop the ends off, if possible, and return all the bones to the stock
- **Optional:** cut off the cartilages, chop or grind them, pulverize the bone ends with a hammer and return the bones and the cartilage to the stock
- Continue simmering for an additional 3 hours
- Add the vegetables the last ½ hour of cooking
- Remove the vegetables, strain the stock and discard the bones and cartilages
- Enjoy consommé or use as a stock for soups or sauces

A NOTE ABOUT STOCKS
If you are a very weak or sensitive patient, you should not use a stock that needs to be reheated. Also make certain that you do not react to the ingredients in any stock you intend to make. It may be a good idea to start with water and incorporate stocks later.

FISH STOCK
Do not discard the cut-offs from fish. Fish soup bases and fish stocks were used to put weaker children and ill adults back on their feet.

Cut-off fish heads, bones, tails, fins and skin
3 c. water per pound of fish cut-offs (there is no exact amount recommended)
1 bay leaf crumbled

- Cook for 45 minutes to 1.5 hours or even longer to extract the nutrients from the bones
- Strain the stock through a sieve or cheesecloth, pressing the content with a wooden spoon

EASY LEEK AND LENTIL OR BARLEY SOUP

1 c. lentils or barley
(or both)
1 leek chopped
3 to 4 c. soup stock
optional: spices and salt
to taste

* Soak the lentils
  overnight or longer,
  strain the water
* Simmer the lentils for
  ½ hour or longer
* Add the leak and
  continue simmering
  for an additional
  ½ hour or longer
* Transfer to a blender
  and purée
* Adjust spices if using
  and serve

**IF USING BARLEY,
DOUBLE OR EVEN
TRIPLE THE INITIAL
COOKING TIME.**

REAL CHICKEN NOODLE OR RICE SOUP
Kids love this soup, and you'll love the versatility of the stock. Make a batch to use in place of water when cooking millet, rice, quinoa and barley. Superior flavour!

1 whole chicken, cut up (gizzards and necks can be included for flavour. Sufficient water to cover (but don't drown it)
¾ c. carrot, chopped into chunks
¾ c. broccoli or kohlrabi, chopped into chunks
¾ c. rutabaga or turnip, chopped into chunks
1 onion, quartered
⅓ c. fresh parsley, about 1 large fistful
⅓ c. fresh dill
5 peppercorns
2 whole garlic cloves, peeled
1 bay leaf
1 T. salt (kosher, pickling, or sea salt is best)

* Wash the chicken and place it in a large stockpot
* Add just enough water to cover the pieces, otherwise your stock will be too diluted to be flavourful
* Bring to a boil
* Use a slotted spoon or turner wrapped with cheesecloth to thoroughly skim off all scum which rises to the top
* Add the root vegetables, spices and salt
* Return to a boil, then reduce heat to low and simmer for 1½ or 2 hours
* Remove the chicken and vegetables, cover and set aside in a warm place to prevent cooling
* Strain the rest of the soup stock through a fine sieve lined with cheesecloth to catch all that stray dill and other bits Ensure you place the sieve over another pot large enough to hold all the liquid
* Discard the sieve contents

PROCEED WITH ONE OF THESE THREE METHODS:

1. STOCK (WITH BONUS SIDE DISHES):
- Use this stock in place of water to cook millet, rice, buckwheat, etc.
- Serve the hot chicken and vegetables as part of a balanced meal

2. CHICKEN NOODLE SOUP:
- Take the chicken off the bone and keep the meat covered in a warm place
- Return the chicken bones to the stock and bring stock to a boil
- Add one cup of small rice pasta (shapes or noodles) or a one-portion measure of rice spaghetti if long noodles are your preference. Do not overcook unless essential – pasta should be al dente. Those with very weak digestion will have to overcook it; it's harder to be a gourmet if your digestion can't tolerate it
- Remove the bones
- Cut the reserved vegetables and chicken into smaller pieces and place back into the stock and pasta to warm up briefly
- Serve immediately

3. CHICKEN RICE SOUP:
- Add ⅓ cup of raw brown rice per 2 cups of stock
- Bring stock to a boil
- Reduce heat and simmer for 45 minutes until rice is tender

EASY VELVETY BUTTERNUT SQUASH SOUP

1 medium squash, peeled and cubed
soup stock double to triple of the squash volume
⅓ t. nutmeg (if not sensitive to it)
salt and pepper to taste

- Simmer the squash and stock for 1 hour
- Add the nutmeg 15 minutes before the end of cooking
- Add salt and pepper to taste
- Transfer to blender and blend
- Serve

THREE-MINUTE BEAN SPROUT SOUP

2 c. bean sprouts
2 eggs or an equivalent amount of minced meat,
3 to 4 T. nuts or seeds ground – optional
1 L. water or a stock if you have one
3 T. parsley, fresh chopped
salt and pepper to taste

- Bring the water or the stock to a boil
- Stir in the meat if using it, and add the bean sprouts and parsley
- Simmer for three minutes
- Mix in the eggs at the end (if not using meat)
- Remove from heat and mix in the nuts or seeds

BUTTERNUT SQUASH SOUP WITH GINGER AND LIME

1 medium onion
4 T. fresh ginger root, peeled and minced or crushed
3 T. butter
1 butternut squash (average size), peeled, seeded and sliced
2 c. chicken or other broth (or water)
2 c. water
3 cloves of garlic, minced
vinegar (or lime if not sensitive to it) to taste
salt and pepper to taste

- In a large pot, sauté the onion and ginger in butter until onion is soft
- Add squash, water, broth and garlic; bring to a boil then simmer covered, for about 20 minutes, or until the squash is very soft
- Purée the mixture in batches in a blender or food processor
- Return to pot, reheat slightly and stir in lime juice/ vinegar, salt and pepper
- Thin with water or chicken broth if required

MILLET, CHICKPEAS, VEGETABLE SOUP

2 t. butter
1 medium onion, diced
2 cloves garlic, minced
1 c. celery, diced
1 c. rutabaga or jicama or radish family vegetable
or other vegetable of your choice, diced
1 c. cooked chickpeas
½ c. millet
1 whole star anise or 3 whole cloves
1½ t. ground cumin
¼ t. turmeric
¼ t. nutmeg
3 lemon slices, preferably organic
(if sensitive to lemon use 3 t. vinegar)
4 c. water
1 t. salt
pinch pepper
2 T. cilantro, chopped

- Sauté onion, garlic and celery in butter over medium heat for 3 minutes or until onion is soft
- Add vegetables, chickpeas, millet, star anise, cumin, turmeric, nutmeg, lemon slices, water, salt and pepper
- Bring to a boil, reduce heat and simmer for 20 minutes or until the millet is cooked
- Remove the lemon slices
- Garnish with cilantro and serve

IF USING AS ALL-IN-ONE-MEAL, CONSIDER ADDING A SOURCE OF PROTEIN.
e.g. mix in:

- *½ c. chopped or minced meat in the last 10 minutes of cooking*
- *2 to 3 beaten eggs in the last few minutes of cooking*
- *¼ to ½ c. roasted nuts or seeds, when garnishing*

OVERNIGHT LENTIL SOUP
Dust off the crock pot and make breakfast and lunch while you sleep. Good food doesn't get much easier!

1½ c. dry lentils
7 c. stock or water
1 medium onion, chopped
1 large rib celery
1 large carrot, diced
1 clove garlic, minced
Optional: ½ to ¾ c. lamb stew meat, chopped into small pieces
4 t. lemon juice, if not irritating
1 t. ground cumin
½ c. fresh parsley, minced
1 T. unsalted butter

- Sort, wash and soak the lentils or dhal (see the *Beans Crash Course* for full details)
- Place lentils, vegetables and garlic into crock pot and cook on low for 8 hours or overnight
  - If you prefer bones and larger pieces of meat in the soup, add them with the lentils
- Add the lemon, cumin, parsley, butter (lamb meat) and simmer for 15 minutes
- Before serving, transfer half the soup to a food processor or blender and purée, then return to the soup pot
- Serve promptly or ladle into thermos bottles for a hot lunch

BLACK BEAN EGG SOUP

1 stalk celery chopped
1 carrot sliced
1 small rutabaga chopped
1 onion chopped
2 T. butter organic
4 c. water or stock if you have one
(add more water as needed)
1 c. black beans soaked overnight or
longer
¼ t. salt or to taste
1 to 2 t. celery seeds
2 T. buckwheat flour
2 T. vinegar (optional)
2 eggs or an equivalent amount of
ground meat

- Melt butter in a large pot and
  lightly sauté the onion and other
  vegetables
- Add beans and enough water to
  cover
- Simmer until the beans are soft
- Purée the mixture in 2 batches if
  necessary
- While puréeing blend in ½ of the
  dry ingredients per batch
- Return to the pot and reheat
- Stir in the ground meat or eggs
  - Break the eggs apart immediately
    after dropping them in the soup
  - Alternatively, drop the eggs in
    carefully and poach them

IMPORTANT:
DO NOT FREEZE
THIS SOUP!

MIXED VEGETABLE SOUP

*If you miss potatoes in your veggie soup,
try this easy 'more or less' recipe. It's also a
tasty way to introduce sea kelp into your diet,
which is immensely nutritious.*

1 or 2 Jerusalem artichokes
2 medium beets chopped
1 c. acorn squash peeled and chopped
1 or 2 T. organic butter, for sautéing
1 large onion, finely chopped
2 or 3 stalks celery, sliced or diced
7 c. stock or water
1 c. fresh green peas or chopped green beans
2 to 3 t. parsley
½ T. sea salt
½ t. each of basil, oregano and sea kelp
cayenne pepper to taste
Optional: 1 stalk broccoli peeled and finely
chopped

- Do not peel the artichoke but cut it into
  small chunks
- Steam the artichoke pieces with the
  vegetables and peas/beans for 10 minutes,
  set aside
- Sauté the onions and celery with sufficient
  oil in a large soup pot until translucent
- Add stock or water and the remainder of
  the ingredients, including the pre-steamed
  veggies, into the sautéed onions and garlic
- Cook on medium-low heat for about
  45 minutes to an hour; vegetables should
  be tender, but not soggy
- Remove 1 to 2 cups of broth and some
  vegetables from the soup
- Purée in a food processor or blender, and
  pour back into the soup; this thickens the
  soup naturally and intensifies the flavours
- Tweak the seasoning of the soup to your
  preference, and add water if a less thick
  soup is wanted
  Optional: Just before serving add 1 or 2 T.
  of flax oil for an added nutritional boost

CREAM OF BROCCOLI OR CAULIFLOWER SOUP

4 c. water
3 c. broccoli or cauliflower, chopped
⅔ c. fresh green peas (shelled) optional
2 c. rice milk
2 eggs
¼ c. oat flour
¼ t. nutmeg
½ t. salt

- Bring salted water to boil and add broccoli or cauliflower
- Cook until soft
- Place in blender and purée until smooth
- Return to the pot, add rice milk, half of the nutmeg and bring to a gentle boil stirring occasionally
- In a soup bowl mix the eggs, oat flour and half of the nutmeg with a fork
- The mixture should have a consistency a bit thicker then a pancake batter
- With a teaspoon, drop the mixture into the boiling soup and whisk
- Cook for 2 minutes

Tip: *Feel free to experiment with using or adding turnip, daikon and other vegetables.*

CREAM OF CARROT SOUP TROPICAL

2 T. butter
1 large onion, chopped
8 to 10 sliced carrots
6 slices of ginger, peeled and crushed
2 c. chicken broth or water
¼ c. brown rice
2 c. rice milk
½ c. unsweetened coconut, shredded
salt to taste
a few sprigs of parsley, cilantro or fresh mint, chopped (optional)

Continued on next page

KIDNEY VEGETABLE SOUP

1 to 2 calf kidneys cut into thin pieces
2 c. turnips chopped
1 c. celery sliced
1 onion medium size, chopped
½ c. green peas fresh (optional)
¼ c. dill chopped
¼ c. vinegar
6 to 8 c. water
3 T. buckwheat or other alternative flour
1 T. oil or organic butter
1 t. salt

- Wash the cut-up kidneys in water; repeat several times, squeezing the water out each time
- **Optional:** Soak them after washing; change the water several times.
- Add the kidneys and vegetables to boiling water
- Simmer until vegetables are soft
- Remove one cup of stock and blend in all remaining ingredients **EXCEPT SALT**
- Return mixture to the soup and blend well
- Continue simmering uncovered until the soup is slightly thickened
- Salt before serving

Note:

Oriental medicine says if you have weaker kidneys eat kidneys!

Some cooks prefer to wash, precook cut-up kidneys and discard the water each time.

FISH CHOWDER
1 c. fish stock or water
2 c. rice or other milk substitute or
fish stock
1 lb. haddock or other cold sea fish
chopped
1 c. squash, diced
1 c. rutabaga, diced small
1 c. celery, chopped
½ c. medium onion, chopped
2 T. organic butter
2 T. parsley fresh, chopped
(or 1 t. dried)
1 bay leaf
¼ t. thyme, dried
¼ t. black pepper
1 t. salt

- In a large pot melt half of the butter
  and sauté the onions till tender
- Add the vegetables and fish stock
  or water
- Cover and simmer for 5 minutes
- Add the fish and spices and cook for
  an additional 10 minutes
- Pour in milk substitute, add fresh
  parsley, if using, and the rest of
  the butter
- Reheat, but do not boil
- Discard the bay leaf before serving

Cream of Carrot Soup Tropical continued from previous page

- Coarsely grind the rice (in a coffee grinder if
  you do not have a grinder)
- Melt butter in a large pot and sauté the onions
  until transparent
- Add carrots, ginger, chicken broth and rice
- Bring to a boil and cook until carrots are soft,
  about 20 minutes, stirring occasionally
- Blend everything in a blender until smooth
- Return to pot, add rice milk and coconut
- Simmer gently for 3 minutes, stirring often
- Add the greens in the last minute of cooking

SOUTHERN PIQUANT FISH SOUP
3 c. fish stock or water (see recipe in
stock section)
1 lb. fish filets cut in pieces
1 turnip, diced
1 medium onion, chopped
1 c. bean sprouts
3 cloves garlic, crushed
3 celery stalks, sliced
1 T. butter organic
½ t. basil, dried
½ t. oregano
2 bay leaves (1 if using a fish stock)
1 t. paprika
½ t. celery seed
½ t. dry mustard
½ t. cilantro, dried
½ t. salt
¼ t. pepper

- In a pot sauté the onions and garlic until transparent
- Add all the vegetables (except bean sprouts), the fish stock
  and spices and simmer for 15 minutes
- Remove half of the volume and blend in a blender
- Return to the pot, add the pieces of fish and cook gently
  for 10 minutes
- Add extra water for thinner soup, if desired
- Add the bean sprouts 3 minutes or less before the
  end of cooking

LENTIL VEGETABLE SOUP OR PURÉE

1 c. lentils or dhal (any kind)
1 to 3 t. butter
1 c. leeks (or an equivalent amount of green onions)
1 to 2 cloves garlic (optional)
2 c. sliced celery
1 c. cauliflower, chopped
2 c. water
¼ t. thyme
¼ t. pepper
¼ t. caraway seeds
½ t. salt or to taste
3 T. sesame seed butter, or ground sesame or flax seeds
Or substitute 1 to 2 t. flax seed oil or canola oil

- Sort, wash and soak the lentils
- Melt butter in large pan
- Sauté the leeks/onions and garlic briefly (1 or 2 minutes)
- Add the celery and cauliflower and continue to sauté for 1 to 3 minutes
- Add 2 cups of water and bring to a boil
- Add lentils, reduce heat and simmer for 20 to 30 minutes, partially covering the pan
- Add the seasonings 10 to 15 minutes before cooking is complete
- Add the sesame seed butter or ground seeds
- Blend, food process, or mash the cooked mixture
- If you want a spread, leave the mixture thick
- Taste, and add more salt, pepper and paprika if desired
- For soup, add more hot water or your favourite stock

Pressure cooker method:

- Start with the same procedure as above, except add the seasonings in with the lentils
- Bring to pressure and turn the heat down to cook for 5 to 10 minutes at the same pressure
- If you want the lentils really soft, cook longer or let the pressure dissipâté slowly (let the cooker stand longer with the lid still on); you then might not need to blend or mash the mixture

SIMPLIFIED LENTIL VEGETABLE SOUP OR PURÉE

Here's how to shave off some preparation time from this recipe:

- *To avoid sautéing, add the onions and garlic to the mixture when adding the green herbs, about 10 to 15 minutes before cooking is complete*

- *Option: add the garlic during the blending process; do not choose this shortcut if sensitive to raw garlic, which many of us are*

- *Add 1 to 2 t. oil or ½ to 1 t. butter during blending; Choose one of these options:*

  - *organic butter*
  - *non-GMO canola oil*
  - *sesame seed oil*
  - *pumpkin seed oil*

Avocado may be mixed into virtually any purée or spread. It may also be used as a topping for grains, beans or cooked vegetables. Avocado is used fresh and uncooked. Add it raw to the cooked food.

Tip: Works well with whole green peas and black or other beans. You may need to increase the cooking time accordingly.

Stir in 2 to 3 eggs or minced meat in the last few minutes of cooking to increase the protein content.

JANICE'S SUPER STEW

1 bunch of washed fresh greens (kale spinach, beet leaves, chard)
2 to 4 c. stock (chicken, bison, lamb or vegetable)
Vary the amount of stock depending on whether a soup or stew consistency is desired
3 cloves garlic, mashed
Fresh rosemary or thyme (a couple of good-sized sprigs)
⅓ c. soaked adzuki beans, French lentils or whole mung beans
½ c. soaked grain such as quinoa, brown rice, wild rice or buckwheat
1 c. (or more if desired) small diced fresh vegetables, such as zucchini, yellow beets, green beans
Very small diced pieces of lamb stew meat, pork stir-fry, chicken breast, ground meat or cut up organic breakfast sausage
Celtic sea salt to taste
Pepper, if desired, to taste

- Remove tough stems from kale, chard and beet leaves, then roughly chop leaves.
- Bring stock to a simmer and add garlic, fresh herbs and beans or lentils
- Add grain of choice as follows:
  - Brown rice – add together with beans and cook mixture for about 30 minutes
  - Other grain – cook above mixture for 15 minutes, then add grain and cook 15 minutes more
- Add other ingredients following the cooking times below:
  - Beets – add during the last 15 minutes of cooking time
  - Green beans – add during the last 10 minutes of cooking time
  - Kale – add during the last 5 minutes of cooking time
  - Meat and softer greens (spinach, chard, or beet greens) – add during the last 3 minutes of cooking time
- Season to taste and enjoy

Hint: Yellow beets are very sweet and add a unique flavour.

Remember:
Those with weak digestion or food sensitivities need to overcook grains, beans and vegetables. Cooking time could be as much as double what is indicated in recipes. See Crash Course in Grains, for more information. Do not overcook meat.

GRAINS CRASH COURSE

32

GRAINS CRASH COURSE

Ratio rule of thumb: Water to grain ratio is 2 to 1 for most grains.

Exception: Millet and barley 2½ c. water per cup of these grains. Sorghum 2½ to 4 c. water per cup of sorghum grain.

Cooking Method: Bring water to a boil, then turn down to low and simmer until tender. This will vary from 12 to 20 minutes for millet, to 55 minutes or even hours for barley. If more liquid is needed, you may add more and continue simmering to the desired level of tenderness.

In spite of the gourmet preference to cook to al dente, those with food sensitivities and weak digestion have to overcook everything except meat. Overcooked, softer grains are easier on our digestive systems than those cooked to al dente. Initially, some people will have to boil grains to mush. This can be achieved in two ways: cooking longer or allowing cooked grains to cool down slowly, stirring more often where applicable.

If you can tolerate al dente cooked grains, reduce cooking time, stir as little as possible, and cool the pot down quickly by placing it in cold water.

Alternatively, you can apply a cold, wet cloth over the lid. If you are using pressure cookers, please consult your owner's manual for safe cool-down tips.

Pre-soakers: Whole barley, oats and rye need to be soaked overnight in a large amount of water. Then drain, add the same amount of stock or water and cook in the manner described earlier. Soaking also reduces cooking time, which is essential for long-cookers like barley. In addition, it tends to deactivate the aggravating lectins in the grains.

Wheat and any grains that belong to the wheat family must be excluded from this eating regimen. However, if you can't give up wheat, try replacing it occasionally with Kamut. Kamut is an ancient grain that is a more nutritious version of wheat. Normally, I recommend that my wheat-sensitive patients eliminate it also.

IF QUICK COOK RICE IS YOUR IDEA OF EATING GRAINS, YOU MIGHT LIKE TO READ THIS SHORT EXCERPT ON THE REAL THING.

Important: All grains must be well washed before use, including rice. Grains are susceptible to fungal growth.

Those who are extra sensitive should cook grains well or overcook them. Some patients have to start with white basmati rice as opposed to the far more nutritious brown rice. The white rice might be less irritating to very sensitive digestive systems.

A NOTE ABOUT RYE: Rye is strong and bitter. For this reason, it is often mixed with other grains to offset its taste. I do not encourage this practice for sensitive patients. Patients with weaker digestion may react to a combination of two or more grains, even if they can tolerate each of them singularly. Instead, I recommend combining rye with beans, vegetables and meats.

Note: *Since most wild rice is not organically grown, it's best to stay with organic brown rice.*

MIXED GRAINS
I recommend using only one grain at a time for those of us who are more sensitive. Adverse reactions are usually seen when mixing barley, oats or rye together or with other grains.

However, it appears to be slightly less allergenic than wheat, not to mention better tasting. Simply stated, if you have to have some wheat, make it Kamut – go with the lesser of two evils.

Wild Rice: Some wild rice needs a short presoak of 2 to 4 hours, while others cook well without soaking. The problem is there's no way of telling ahead of time. If after 1½ hours the rice is still too firm, turn off the heat and allow to cool. Then start again like you would with uncooked brown rice. Mark the bag so you know to presoak next time!

Brown rice should be stored in your refrigerator because it quickly goes rancid. Always smell the rice before cooking it – if there's an off aroma, don't take the chance. Don't buy such large quantities that you can't get through it in six months.

Variations
- For a sweet version, try adding chopped fruits while porridge is simmering
- For a non-sweet version, try adding chopped vegetables and minced meat while porridge is cooking
- An egg can be added when cooking is complete for either the sweet or non-sweet version, or as the only added ingredient to the cooked grain

Topping suggestions
Powdered cocoa, ground poppy seeds, shredded coconut, seeds or nuts, seed or nut butter, flax seed oil or rice syrup

PORRIDGES

QUICK ROASTED PORRIDGE FROM ANY GRAIN
Quick, exceedingly versatile and great tasting no matter what you do, roasted porridges can be served with any of the following: nuts, seeds, fruits, eggs, beans or meat.

½ to 1 c. ground grains (millet, rice, buckwheat, oats)
1 t. to 1 T. butter
dash of salt
water, as required
Optional: 1 to 2 c. milk alternative (nut, seed or any other milk alternative, or even a herbal tea), and seasonings to taste (cinnamon or cloves, for a sweet taste)
- Grind the grains to flour in a coffee or grain grinder
- Melt butter in a cast iron pan or deep skillet with a thick bottom
- Dust flour over the butter while stirring
- Roast the flour and butter mixture briefly, stirring constantly
- Continue stirring and add ½ to 1 c. water or liquid
- Bring to a boil
- Reduce the heat and simmer until cooked, stirring frequently, adding a bit more liquid of your choice if required
  - Soft grains or very fine flour may take less than two minutes to cook, while harder grains or coarser flours take a bit longer
- Season as desired before serving

SLOW ROASTED PORRIDGE FROM ANY GRAIN
Ingredients and procedure as in Quick Roasted Porridge, except:

- Before dusting in the flour and while stirring add
  - 1T. to ½ medium onion, chopped
  - 1 to 2 cloves minced garlic
- Sauté for ½ to 1 minute
- Continue with Quick Roasted Porridge recipe

RICE, RICE PILAF AND PASTA

WILD AND BROWN RICE
This tasty side dish is also great as a wheat-free stuffing for poultry or baked ribs.

2 c. cooked brown and wild rice blend (try 1½ c. brown
and ½ c. wild)
2 stalks celery, diced
1 medium onion, diced
1 T. olive oil or butter
¼ c. sliced almonds (omit or substitute another nut if sensitive)
dash pepper
¼ t. salt, if desired
½ t. dried sage (or more if you love the taste)
½ t. fresh rosemary (or ¼ t. dried, in a pinch)
¼ c. fresh parsley, chopped
⅛ c. fresh thyme
Homemade poultry stock or water

- Cook the rice as usual, using stock or water; the wild and brown rice may need to be cooked separately, or the faster cooking one may be added later
- Meanwhile, sauté the celery and onion over medium heat in 1 T. extra virgin olive oil or organic butter (increase amount if necessary to facilitate cooking)
- When the vegetables are almost tender, add the seasonings and nuts, if using
- Continue to sauté for another minute or two, not allowing the blend to burn
- Serve hot

If using as a stuffing:

- Cool to room temperature before stuffing the poultry
- You may moisten the stuffing with a little more stock or rice milk to make it cling together

Tip: For variety, try adding caraway seeds, marjoram, oregano and salt to your porridge.

Hint: For more protein, add eggs, nut or seed butter, minced or chopped meat, fish or poultry.

Hint: Overdoing it on rosemary gives a 'pine' taste to your food.

Warning:

Never place hot stuffing into raw poultry and never pre-stuff any dish.

*Stuffed poultry and meats should be placed **immediately** into a preheated oven.*

TROPICAL BROWN RICE PILAF

A tasty recipe that's easily changed for variety and limited only by your imagination.

4 t. butter
1 chopped onion
1 minced clove garlic
1½ c. parsnips, thinly sliced
1 c. brown rice
1½ c. chicken stock
⅛ t. cinnamon
⅛ t. allspice
¼ t. pepper
½ c. raisins or currants
2 T. chopped fresh parsley for garnish

- In a heavy frying pan, melt butter over medium heat
- Cook onion, garlic and parsnips, stirring occasionally for about 6 minutes or until parsnips are almost tender
- Add rice and stir to coat
- Add water or chicken stock, the three spices and the raisins or currants
- Bring to a boil
- Reduce heat to a simmer, cover and cook for 45 minutes or until rice is tender and liquid is absorbed
- Fluff with a fork to separate the grains
- Garnish with parsley

RICE PASTA WITH SWISS CHARD

And here you thought you had to give up mac & cheese! This is healthiest served with a more acidic side dish, such as lentils.

2 lbs. rice pasta of any kind
½ c. extra virgin olive oil
2 garlic cloves, minced
½ c. grated almond cheese
(Swiss flavour is our favourite)
salt and pepper to taste
6 c. cooked, chopped Swiss chard or spinach
2 t. dried tarragon
3 T. lemon juice
½ c. butter
salt
wheat-free bread crumbs, toasted
Optional: parmesan cheese substitute

- Steam Swiss chard or spinach; chop and keep warm
- Cook rice pasta until al dente or overcook for weak/sensitive digestion; drain
- Mix pasta with oil, garlic, cheese substitute and seasonings
- Lightly grease a 9" x 13" oblong pan
- Spread hot greens over the bottom
- Place noodles on top and sprinkle with breadcrumbs and parmesan substitute, if using
- Broil for 5 minutes to toast the crumbs and ensure dish is warm throughout

COCONUT RICE

Missing the tropical taste? Try this.

1 c. brown or white rice (either the jasmine or basmati varieties are best)
2 c. coconut milk
Optional: 1 t. coconut butter/oil or organic non-GMO flax or canola oil

- Cook the rice as usual, using coconut milk instead of stock or water
- Stir in the oil, if using, when rice is cooked

HIMALAYAN BARLEY AND BROWN RICE

Barley and rice belong to the same family. Despite the need for sensitive people to use caution when mixing grains, I simply can't refrain from including this recipe.

1 c. brown rice
¼ c. barley
¼ t. salt
2½ c. water (or follow your pressure cooker guide)

- Wash the barley and rice
- Starting with cold, salted water, bring the water and grains to a boil (if using a pressure cooker, bring to pressure)
- Lower heat and continue cooking until done
- If you are more sensitive, overcook to a soft, creamy texture and let sit for a few minutes before taking the lid off or opening the pressure-cooker

When I was treating people in remote villages in the Himalayan foothills, locals fed me their barley which tasted somewhat like rice. Since it was memorably delicious, I tried to recreate this taste by combining rice and barley together.

VARIATION: SWEETER VERSION OF BROWN RICE OR MILLET

One or both of these grains together can be cooked with squash and optional daikon to add a sweeter flavour.

1 to 2 c. grains
1 c. squash, diced
¼ c. daikon (optional)
pinch of salt

Optional spices, alone or in combinations. Experiment with the amounts and adapt to your taste:

Pinch of cinnamon
Pinch of cloves
Pinch of cardamom (watch for sensitivities)
Pinch of licorice root

- Proceed as in the original Himalyan recipe
- Add the cut vegetables and spices at the same time as the grains

Serve with any combination of the following: lentils, dhal, chickpeas, roasted or ground nuts and seeds.

VARIATION: BROWN RICE AND MILLET

This combination also provides a uniquely pleasant flavour. The grain amounts and cooking process are the same as for Brown Rice and Barley except it uses more water and cooking time is shortened. Please consult your pressure cooker's manual to make these adjustments, and use your best judgement.

HOT AND FAST BARLEY OR RYE WITH DRIED BERRIES

The breakfast that makes itself (almost). Prepare it on your day off.

⅓ c. organic rolled barley or rye flakes
pinch of salt
⅔ c. boiling water
1 t. flax oil or organic non-GMO canola oil
Optional: Dried berries are a quick and satisfying addition to this porridge. So are rice syrup and cinnamon.

• If using frozen berries, defrost your serving size and set aside. (⅓ c. is a guideline for blueberries)
• Place the barley or rye in boiling water and continute to boil and stir, until the grain softens
• Turn burner off, stir in berries, cover and let stand until water absorbs and grain is soft
• Stir in the oil and add cinnamon and rice syrup, if desired
• Alternative milk is optional if you like the old-fashioned 'oats in a moat'

If you want a larger or smaller serving, simply maintain the 1 to 2 ratio of flakes to water.

VARIATION

Hot and Fast Barley can be made savory versus sweet. Just add your choice of seasonings, meat, eggs, beans and vegetables. Eggs, vegetables, and to some extent minced meat, can be cooked in the same pot.

This meal is healthier served with some form of protein like nuts/seeds or their milks/butters. Other options are cooked beans such as chickpeas or lentils.

BARLEY, PILAF AND PORRIDGE

Very sensitive individuals need to cook barley until its very soft. If you are more tolerant, you may enjoy it 'al dente'. Barley may be cooked the same way as rice with a bit of salt, and/or with spices and herbs. You can also substitute rye.

PRESSURE-COOKED BARLEY

When cooked properly, barley is very delicious. It's similar to rice in that it can settle the digestion and absorb toxins. Another added benefit is that barley is usually much cheaper than rice.

½ to ¾ c. barley
1 small onion, or ½ of a medium onion, or an equal amount of green onions
¼ to ½ t. seaweed, such as kelp, nori, or dulse (if you're uncertain about seaweed, leave it for the next time you try this recipe)
salt to taste

• Wash and soak the barley overnight or for 5 to 8 hours
• Cook all ingredients in a pressure cooker for up to one hour:
  • Start with high heat to bring the pressure up to the recommended level
  • Turn the heat down to maintain the pressure
• When the time is up, remove cooker from heat and, without opening it, cool the cooker under cold water
• If a soft, creamy consistency is desired (which is easier on the digestion), let the pressure dissipâté without dousing the cooker in cold water before opening
• If a firmer texture is wanted, reduce the cooking time accordingly, cool down and open the cooker promptly

Serve as you would rice. Excellent accompaniments are beans, vegetables, roasted nuts and seeds or meat.

BARLEY NUT PILAF
A delicious side dish that's a nice change from rice and a healthy substitute for potatoes.

1 c. pot barley
¼ c. butter, divided
⅓ c. whole pine nuts or macadamia nuts chopped coarsely
1 c. diced onion
½ c. finely minced parsley
½ t. basil leaves
¼ t. ground black pepper
3 c. homemade stock or water

- Rinse the barley in cold water and drain well
- In a frying pan melt 2 T. of the butter over medium heat
- Add the nuts and stir until lightly toasted
- Remove nuts with a slotted spoon and set aside
- Add the remaining butter, melt and cook onion for 2 or 3 minutes or until soft
- Add the barley and cook, stirring until lightly toasted
- Remove from heat, stir in nuts, parsley, basil and pepper
- Place in a 1½ quart casserole
- Heat the stock until boiling, pour over barley and stir well to blend
- Cover and bake for 1½ hours at 375°F (Glass casseroles require heat to be reduced by 25 degrees)
- After 1 hour, stir well and continue baking for the remaining half-hour

BUCKWHEAT

QUICK BUCKWHEAT PORRIDGE WITH EGGS AND VEGETABLES
Healthier breakfasts are not sweet.

⅓ to ½ c. buckwheat (may be replaced with barley or rye flakes)
1 c. water (increase amount for longer soaking or softer consistency)
1 to 2 eggs
½ c. chopped vegetables of your choice, (rutabaga, kale, turnip)
¼ t. basil
1 t. or more of oil: flaxseed, hemp seed, or sesame seed
Optional: ⅛ to ¼ t. powdered caraway seeds or black pepper
salt to taste.

Continued on next page

MANY PEOPLE REACT ADVERSELY TO BARLEY. IT MIGHT BE A GOOD IDEA TO START WITH A SMALL AMOUNT OF OVERCOOKED BARLEY.

Note:
Highly sensitive patients might not tolerate caraway seeds or black pepper.

Continued from previous page

- Wash and soak the buckwheat overnight
- Boil the water, add seasonings, salt and buckwheat
  - Add longer-cooking vegetables at this time, e.g. turnip
- Boil for about 5 minutes, stirring occasionally until the buckwheat is soft
  - Quick-cooking vegetables are added now according to their required cooking time, e.g. kale
- Break an egg into the mixture in the last minute or two of cooking and stir to incorporate
- Cook until vegetables and buckwheat are soft
- Stir in oil just before serving

SUSAN'S WHEAT-FREE TABBOULEH

A hypoallergenic version of the refreshing Lebanese favourite.

1 c. cooked millet
⅓ c. chopped green onions
About 15 fresh mint leaves, chopped
¼ c. chopped parsley
¼ carrot, grated
1 stalk celery, finely chopped
Salt to taste
3 to 4 T. of your favourite vinaigrette (or white wine vinegar)
Romaine leaves

- Replacing water with chicken broth, prepare millet; see instructions on this page
- Combine all ingredients using sufficient vinaigrette to moisten millet
- Do not chill the tabbouleh
- Place tabbouleh in center of plate and encircle with lightly steamed romaine lettuce

Serves 4 to 5 portions as an hors d'oeuvre or 2 to 3 portions as a salad course.

MILLET

Millet is a perfect replacement for corn, rice or other grains. Its mild taste lends itself to both sweet and savory recipes. Millet's softness is easy to regulate with the amount of water used in cooking as well as with the length of cooking and/or cooling off times. Millet requires more water than rice and can be easily cooked to a liquid consistency.

BASIC MILLET COOKED SIMPLY

1 c. millet
2½ c. water
pinch of salt
Optional:
Seasonings such as curry, turmeric, coriander, cumin, oregano, thyme, caraway seeds, etc.
or
Sweeteners and complementary spices such as cinnamon, cloves, etc.

- Rinse millet, drain and add to salted water
- Mix in the optional seasonings
- Bring to a boil, reduce heat and simmer for 12 to 20 minutes, do not stir
- Turn the heat off and let stand until water is absorbed
- Add sweetener if using

Serve with any of the following: vegetables, beans, nuts, seeds, meat, eggs.

QUINOA

Quinoa, a delicious and versatile grain, is my preferred choice in soups as a replacement for pasta or potatoes. Quinoa cooks faster, tastes better and is healthier.

SAVORY QUINOA
1 c. quinoa
2 c. water
1 clove garlic, minced
¼ t. oregano
¼ t. thyme
(other herbs or spices may be substituted to your taste)
pinch of salt
½ to 1 t. butter

- Wash and drain quinoa (let stand in an elevated strainer to maximize water drainage)
- Melt the butter and sauté garlic for about 1 or 2 minutes
- While stirring, add the quinoa and keep sautéeing for 5 or more minutes until quinoa starts to brown
- Meanwhile, bring the water to a boil in a medium pot
- Pour the sautéed quinoa and garlic into the water
- Add seasonings and salt
- Simmer until done, about 15 minutes or less
- Turn the heat off and let stand for 5 minutes

Serve with your choice of stir-fried vegetables, beans, meat, eggs, nuts or seeds.

BASIC QUINOA COOKED SIMPLY
1 c. quinoa
2 c. water
pinch of salt
Optional: Seasonings such as oregano, thyme, caraway seeds, etc. or sweeteners and complementary spices such as cinnamon, cloves, etc.

- Rinse quinoa, drain and add to salted water
- Bring to a boil, reduce heat and simmer for 5 to 10 minutes
- Add the optional seasonings
- Simmer until water is absorbed
- Add sweetener if desired (savory versions are healthier)

Serve with any of the following: vegetables, beans, nuts, seeds, meat, eggs.

SIMPLIFIED VERSION:
- Follow recipe above, but start the process by sautéing fast cooking legumes, e.g. dhal, pink lentils or French lentils together with quinoa
- Add your choice of vegetables and meat during the last 10 minutes or less of cooking time, depending on what you are using

HOT QUINOA BREAKFAST
Bored of the same breakfast cereals? Quinoa is another quick cooking grain that's great in the morning, or any other part of the day.

1 c. quinoa
2 c. water
⅓ c. dried fruit or ½ c. cooked fruit
⅓ c. nuts or seed ground (optional and not necessary if served with nut or seed butter)
½ t. cinnamon
⅛ t. salt

- Rinse quinoa, drain and add to salted water
- Bring to a boil, reduce heat and simmer for 5 to 10 minutes
  - Cooked quinoa becomes translucent
- Add dried fruit and cinnamon
- Simmer until water is absorbed
- Makes 2 servings

Serve with milk alternative, nut or seed butter and sweeten to taste with rice syrup.

TEFF

BASIC TEFF COOKED SIMPLY
1 c. teff
2 to 4 c. water (depending on the consistency desired)
Optional: pinch of salt

- Wash and drain the teff
- Bring the salted water to a boil, then pour in teff
- Reduce heat, cover and simmer until done and water is absorbed, 10 to 20 minutes, depending on softness desired
  - Stir occasionally toward the end of the cooking time
- Remove from heat, cover and let stand for five minutes or less depending on the softness desired

Serve with beans, vegetables, meat and eggs, or with fruit, nuts and seeds when a sweet taste is required.

THANKS TO DR. DICK THOM, N.D., DDS., AUTHOR OF "COPING WITH FOOD INTOLERANCES" FOR ALLOWING US TO MODIFY HIS TEFF RECIPES FOR THIS BOOK.

AMARANTH

BASIC AMARANTH
1 c. amaranth
Optional:
medium onion, finely chopped
crushed cloves garlic, finely chopped
¼ t. each of your choice of spices or green culinary herbs
(1 to 3 seasonings)
¼ t. salt, or to taste
3 to 4 c. filtered water (4 c. for softer amaranth, 3 c. for al dente)

- Wash and drain the amaranth
- Boil the water, then add the amaranth, salt, onions and spices
  (do not add green culinary herbs)
- Reduce heat and simmer for about 20 to 25 minutes until the
  water is absorbed, stirring occasionally
- In the last 10 minutes of cooking, add your choice of green
  culinary herbs and the garlic

Serve with beans, meat or eggs and vegetables.

SORGHUM

SORGHUM COOKED SIMPLY
1 c. sorghum grain
2½ to 4 c. water

- Wash and strain the grain
- Soak overnight (optional)
- Boil or steam for 20 to 40 minutes

SORGHUM PORRIDGE
1 c. sorghum flour
4 to 5 c. water or milk alternative (or their combination)
2 T. sorghum molasses or rice syrup (optional)

- Use sorghum flour or grind whole sorghum into fine flour
- Mix flour with 1 to 2 c. of water
- Let soak for at least a few minutes or up to overnight (optional)
- Bring the rest of the water to boil
- Gradually add the flour/water mixture to the boiling water
  while stirring
- Simmer for 10 to 15 minutes stirring as required to prevent sticking

Tip: Use spices and culinary herbs to enhance the taste.

Serve the Sorghum as you would any other porridge.

CRASH COURSE IN BEANS AND LEGUMES

33

DRY LEGUMES CRASH COURSE

Although cooking with dried beans takes a little foresight, they are far healthier and better tasting than the soggy, sodium-ridden canned ones. Avoid canned beans and any other canned foods. They contain a fraction of their original nutrients since many vital ones are destroyed in the canning process. In addition, canning increases levels of cancer-causing substances such as exogenous estrogens.

Please bear in mind that some people have poor tolerance of beans. The following cooking method usually reduces digestive difficulties. In any case, it takes awhile for the body to develop the specific enzymes necessary to digest beans. Note that chickpeas are actually beans.

THE PROCESS:

- **Wash and Sort:** Toss the dried legumes into a colander or a strainer and pick out discoloured or damaged ones and anything else that looks inedible and foreign. Run water over the legumes shaking the colander as you do so.

- **Soak:** 1 c. of dry beans, peas, lentils or dhal should soak, un-covered in 4 c. of room-temperature water. Changing the water at least once or twice during the soak will reduce gas.

Soaking Times:
- Beans or peas: at least 8 hours
- Chickpeas, navy beans and adzuki beans: 12 to 48 hours
- Lentils and small dhal: at least a few hours or overnight

- **Drain:** To reduce gas, it is imperative that you discard the water that legumes have soaked in.

- **Rinse:** Legumes should be rinsed several times in fresh water; agitate them as you rinse.

- **Place:** Add fresh water to a pot until the legumes are covered by about 1 inch of water (1 cup of legumes needs 2 cups of water).

Note:

Fresh beans or peas, frozen beans or peas, sprouted beans, pink lentils or very small dhal (smaller than lentils), in that order, are usually less difficult to digest than other beans. Consider preparing these varieties first when reintroducing beans into your diet. Dry pink lentils and small dhal are easy to cook and virtually dissolve.

FOR LESS SENSITIVE PATIENTS: BEANS ARE DONE WHEN YOU CAN EASILY CRUSH THEM IN YOUR MOUTH WITH YOUR TONGUE.

- **Cook:** Bring legumes to a boil uncovered over high heat. Skim the foam off the top of the water, as this froth also causes gas. Turn heat to very low, so the beans are barely bubbling. If you cook them too fast, they will be tough.

- **Change the water:** In the last 15 minutes of cooking, replace the water with fresh water sufficient to cover the legumes by at least 1 inch. Return to a simmer.

- **Add spices or herbs:** Add salt at the last minute, as it will toughen the beans. To aid in digestibility and flavour, you may now add culinary herbs of your choice. See the *Culinary Herbs and Spices* section for more information on gas-reducing herbs.

- **Continue simmering until done:** The cooking time may vary from 60 to 90 minutes for the longer-cooking beans, to less than 20 minutes for pink lentils and small yellow dhal.

Many culinary herbs reduce gas and improve our ability to expel the gas. Cooking beans with Kombu is used for this purpose. See the section 'Medicinal Herbs in the Kitchen'.

THOSE WITH SENSITIVE DIGESTIVE SYSTEMS MUST OVERCOOK BEANS, DHAL, LENTILS AND PEAS, EVEN TO THE POINT THAT THEY MAY DISSOLVE. YOU MAY ALSO MASH THEM TO ASSIST DIGESTION.

COOKING TIME GUIDE:

The cooking times suggested below can be changed to achieve your preferred level of tenderness.

Adzuki, navy, pinto beans or chickpeas	60 to 90 minutes
Whole peas	40 minutes
Split peas	30 minutes
Lentils and small dhal	15 to 20 minutes
Other beans	30 to 60 minutes

Yield Generally: 1 cup of dried beans or legumes will yield at least 2 cups cooked.

COOKED SPROUTED BEANS

Very sensitive patients should start out eating the sprout only, not the attached bean. If there is no adverse reaction, try both the beans and their sprouts.

2 c. whole sprouted beans, or the sprouts only enough water to cover
• Add the sprouted beans/sprouts to boiling water
• Reduce heat, cover and simmer until tender
More sensitive people:
   • Simmer longer, partially covered
Less sensitive people:
   • Quick-boiling or briefly submerging bean sprouts in boiling water cooks them sufficiently
• Add salt once cooked

COOKED FRESH BEANS

BEAN SALAD WITH NUTS
1 clove of garlic crushed and finely chopped
½ c. fresh pea pods, chopped into two-inches pieces, or fresh sweet peas
½ c. fresh yellow wax beans chopped into two-inches pieces (you can substitute other yellow and white beans or double the amount of pea pods)
¼ c. mint fresh or cilantro fresh whole (tied in a bouquet)
2 T. mayonnaise (see my recipe)
1 small cucumber peeled and diced
several large lettuce or beet leaves (to cover the bottom of 2 to 3 serving plates)
¼ c. walnuts or other nuts chopped or ground (roasted)
NO PEANUTS
Optional: substitute nuts with sesame seeds (brown, black or wild) or hemp or other seeds
salt to taste

• Mix garlic, mayonnaise and salt in mixing dish (set aside)
• In a sufficiently large pot bring water to a boil
• Add beans and cook for 4 to 6 minutes until tender
• Add cucumber and mint/cilantro and cook 1 to 2 minutes
• Place the lettuce leaves in a strainer and quickly submerge in the boiling water until wilted

Continued on next page

Continued from previous page

- Remove the lettuce leaves and the mint/cilantro, let drain
- Place the lettuce on the serving plates
- Strain the beans and cucumbers
- Chop the mint/cilantro and add to beans
- Place on the top of the leaves, drizzle with mayonnaise mixture
- Sprinkle with ground nuts/seeds and garnish with mint or cilantro

Serve as is or with another protein food: meat, fish or boiled eggs. Can be used as a topping for grains, pancakes, as a filling for a wraps or with non-wheat crackers/tortillas.

SAUTÉED FRESH STRING BEANS

2 c. string beans of any kind
(yellow, green, white)
1 to 2 t. butter or clarified butter
2 to 3 cloves of garlic, minced
1 small onion or ½ medium onion
Optional: ⅛ t. each of black pepper and paprika, or season to taste
2 t. lemon juice (or try a substitute of
1 t. balsamic vinegar if sensitive to lemon)
salt to taste

- Snip off the bean ends
- Melt the butter in a pan
- Add garlic and sauté for 2 minutes
- Add the optional spices, stir briefly, then add the string beans
- While stirring the mixture, add lemon juice and salt
- Cook until tender
  - Crisp-tender takes less than 5 minutes
  - Tender beans take longer, test for doneness

GREEN BEAN, CHESTNUT AND ASPARAGUS SALAD

½ lb. pea pods fresh, cut into two-inch pieces
½ to ⅔ c. water chestnuts, peeled and sliced (if not available use radishes or daikon radish)
½ lb. asparagus, diagonally cut in two-inch lengths
½ c. sesame seed ground or sesame seed butter
black pepper, cayenne/chili pepper and salt to taste

- Bring water (with a pinch of salt) to boil in a steamer
- Place the vegetables in the steamer and steam until tender
- Mix sesame seeds/sesame seed butter, pepper, cayenne or chili pepper and salt and drizzle over the vegetable salad

Note:

- Very sensitive patients might have to overcook the beans initially and delete potentially irritating ingredients
- If concerned about potentially allergenic spices, use celery, parsley, or milder dry herbs such as oregano and sage. Fresh fennel is an option, but some people may react to it just as much as to fennel seeds

ONE DISH LEGUME AND GRAIN MEALS

34

ONE DISH MILLET AND LENTILS
Fast, simple and all-in-one.

¼ to ⅓ c. small dhal (lentils)
½ to ¾ c. millet

- Sort dhal discarding shrivelled and discoloured lentils
- Wash thoroughly dhal and millet by changing the water several times as advised in our Crash Course
  - Soak the dhal before cooking to improve digestibility and reduce the cooking time; soak for a few hours, or overnight if time allows
- Cook this dhal in fresh water until foam forms
- Strain the water, replace with fresh water
- Add the millet, bring the mixture to a boil
- Reduce the heat, and simmer partially covered for 12 to 20 minutes
- Millet will be cooked and small dhal will dissolve
- For fluffier millet, let the cooked mixture stand, covered, or cook a bit longer to allow the millet to absorb any excess water
- Add salt and seasonings to taste.

Serve with stir-fried vegetables and protein of your choice.

SIMPLIFIED VERSION:
Add your choice of diced meat, vegetables and spices about five minutes before the end of cooking. This reduces both the meat stir-frying task and the number of pots to wash up.

VARIATIONS WITH OTHER GRAINS AND LEGUMES
¼ to ½ c. legumes (dried beans, larger lentils, dried peas)
½ to ¾ c. grains (rice, millet, buckwheat, barley)

- Follow the same procedure as above, using our Crash Courses as guidance for soaking and cooking times
- Grains (soaking is optional)
- Beans (soaking is mandatory, the simplest way is overnight)
- Add salt and culinary herbs or spices of your choice during the last ten minutes of cooking
- Cook until both beans and grains are done

Serve with stir-fried vegetables and meat or nuts of your choice.

VEGETABLE CRASH COURSE

35

VEGETABLE BASICS

STEPS TO REDUCE NUTRIENT LOSSES:

* Do not precut and store
* Submerge leafy vegetables in cold water for a few seconds before cleaning
* Use cold water and a natural bristle brush to scrub vegetables
* Wash and cut vegetables just before cooking (cut and transfer directly to the boiling water or hot butter/oil)
* Do not remove the skin if soft – the most nutrient-rich part of the veggie is the skin and the part directly under it (this is another reason to buy organic)
* Cut them into smaller pieces to reduce the cooking time
* For boiling: bring the water to a boil first and boil briefly (to allow some oxygen to escape from the water) then add the vegetables
* For stir-frying: heat the butter then add the vegetables
* Add vegetables to recipes during the last minutes of cooking
    * Harder vegetables are added before the softer ones
    * The longer you cook the vegetables, the softer and easier to digest they will become
* Serve cooked food immediately:
    * Leaving cooked food sit will progressively reduce its nutrient value
    * As mentioned earlier, 'holding time' nutrient losses can easily exceed any losses which might occur during cooking
    * Do not store cooked vegetables

KIDS AND BREAKING THE POTATO HABIT

* Use squash and cauliflower, which are two of the best potato substitutes.

* Experiment with different kinds of squash such as butternut or acorn squash, cooked and mashed with onion, cauliflower and/or different vegetables. Or try slicing squash into 'French Fries' and stir-frying or baking them with a brush of butter and some seasoning. You'll have the most success if you combine and prepare the substitutes in ways that mimic potatoes.

* Gradually add other stir-fried vegetables to the mix. This is also a great intermediary step to getting your kids to eat new steamed or boiled veggies.

* A last resort: gradually introduce a bit of the squash, cauliflower of other vegetables into the mashed potatoes instead of going 'cold turkey'.

Variation: *Grate in ¼ c. of cheese substitute during the mashing process. A great way to get your kids to eat cauliflower*

Note:
Very sensitive Blood type O patients may react adversely to cauliflower if it's insufficiently cooked.

TATER TERMINATOR
Substitute cauliflower for that most popular of nightshades, potatoes.

1 c. cauliflower
1 t. garlic, crushed or minced, just before adding it in
1 to 2 t. organic butter
⅓ c. milk alternative or as required for creamy consistency
salt, pepper and paprika to taste

- Wash cauliflower, break off florets and chop stems if using
- Boil or preferably steam the cauliflower until well done
- Mash with butter, garlic, salt and pepper as you would mashed potatoes, adding a splash of milk substitute to enhance creaminess
  - Since cauliflower does not turn glutinous like potatoes if over-whipped, you can mash it with your food processor or electric mixer
  - Top each serving with a dash of paprika for a nice touch

ASPARAGUS FROM AN OVEN
2 c. asparagus, fresh
2 t. organic butter
pinch pepper, salt
Optional: spices of your choice

- Preheat the oven to 300°F
- Use a baking dish that can be covered with a lid
- Spread the butter on the asparagus and lay the asparagus in one or two layers
- Add salt and spices
- Bake for 20 to 30 minutes depending on the softness desired

Serve as you would potatoes or any other vegetable. Also try dipping them in sauces and spreads.

PARSNIP TATO
Historically, parsnip was considered a prized vegetable and was consumed with both sweet and savoury condiments. Its use predates the use of potatoes.

2 parsnips sliced
1 carrot sliced
Optional: ⅓ to ½ c. kohlrabi chopped
2 to 3 t. organic butter if <u>stir-frying</u> the vegetables
2 T. water

2 T. oil if <u>steaming</u> the vegetables
½ t. dry dill or 1 t. fresh dill
pinch of salt

- Stir-fry the vegetables in butter for 2 to 3 minutes; see my *Crash Course in Stir-Frying*
- Add the spices at the last minute, just before adding the water (the water is added at the last minute of stir-frying to generate steam and to finish cooking)

- Alternatively steam the vegetables until desired softness is achieved
- Add the spices and salt early in the cooking
- Use the oil as a topping

WILTED SALAD CRASH COURSE

36

WARM SALADS? HERE'S WHY...

The purpose of warming salad greens and vegetables is to soften the fiber and to change its cooling quality to warming. The raw vegetable fiber is too coarse for our digestive system and warming foods are easier to digest for weaker people. (See the chapter on Wisdom Versus Common Dogma).

Those with weaker digestions need to cook the vegetables longer to wilt them more. Others can cook them briefly. Quick exposure to heat is often enough to wilt the vegetables and make them tolerable for sensitive digestive systems. It also reduces the nutritional losses caused by prolonged cooking.

Wilting can be done by:

* Brief steaming
* Brief stir-frying
* Adding the vegetables into the wok or skillet just before pouring in the water (for more information, read the *Crash Course in Stir-Frying*)
* Brief submersion in boiling water (use a strainer)
* Pouring hot water, liquid or oil over the vegetables

General approach:

* The length of cooking/wilting time is determined by the hardness of vegetables
* Slice the hard vegetables into long thin strips or peel them with a peeler into long strips so they can be wilted together with the soft vegetables
* Wilt the soft leafy ones in a strainer by briefly submerging in boiling water
* Transfer to the serving bowl and toss; serve immediately while warm; do not stir when incorporating additional ingredients
* To preserve the crunchy texture of the vegetables, steam them very briefly
* Wilted greens should be served with some protein food for a more complete meal: add sliced cooked eggs, meat, nuts/seeds and their butters or beans

TRY USING...
* Soft leafy vegetables
* Hard root vegetables
* Sprouts
* Edible flowers – dandelion tops are the easiest to find
* Butter for the wok or skillet
* Spices, cooking herbs, mustard
* Vinegar
* Garlic/onion
* Salt

SPINACH AND SPROUTS WILTED SALAD

6 c. fresh spinach (torn to bite size pieces)
1 c. bean sprouts
1 to 2 c. beet tops (torn to bite size pieces)
½ c. water chestnuts sliced (or cubed radishes, daikon, jicama)
¼ c. onion finely chopped
½ c. water
3 T. balsamic vinegar (optional)
1 T. butter organic
2 cloves garlic (minced)
pepper or other spices to taste

- Place spinach, sprouts and beet tops in a large bowl and toss
- Preheat skillet or a wok and coat it with butter
- Lightly stir-fry water chestnuts, onion and garlic, starting with the water chestnuts and adding onions and garlic later
- Place the spinach, sprouts and beet tops into the skillet or wok
- Stir very briefly and pour a ½ cup of water with vinegar over it
- Cover with a lid long enough to wilt the sprouts, spinach and beet tops
- Transfer to the serving bowl and toss
- Serve before it cools

CRASH COURSE IN MEAT PREPARATION

Overcooked meat is hard to digest, less flavourful and has lost many of its nutrients.

Tender meat, or that which is minced or cut into small pieces, cooks faster than vegetables. If time is a concern, opt for minced meats.

Game and tougher meats need longer, slower cooking and are perfect for crock pots. Alternatively, you can use a tenderizing mallet or cut meat into smaller pieces, which are better nutrient-saving options.

FRYING AND OIL/FAT DAMAGE

The high heat used for frying, deep frying and to some extent stir-frying, damages all fats. The greatest damage is done to Essential Fatty Acids, the good fats. However, any oil can produce toxic and carcinogenic compounds if heated too high and for too long.

Ideally, avoid frying and deep-frying. Instead use steaming, boiling, baking, or a healthier method of stir-frying and braising (please see relevant Crash Courses).

It is usually very easy to adapt recipes that require frying to a healthier cooking method. You can use the same ingredients, but should replace the saturated fats or oils used for frying. These products have a low amount of Essential Fatty Acids and can be easily replaced by healthy oils high in Essential Fatty Acids. These oils are added when the food is done or, at the very end of the cooking time.

Those who insist on frying foods should use saturated fats – butter, coconut butter/oil, lard or other oils low in Essential Fatty Acids because saturated fats are less damaged by heat.

TIPS ON REDUCING HEAT DAMAGE WHEN FRYING VEGETABLES
- Cut vegetables
- Preheat the pan or wok
- Spread vegetables evenly on the pan/wok bottom
  - Adding the vegetables to the pan before the fats reduces the temperature of the frying surface
  - Stir quickly without fat to prevent vegetables from sticking to the pan/wok bottom
- Add the fat and quick-fry or stir-fry the vegetables
- At completion, pour in a bit of water to finish
  - Put on a lid to trap the steam and finish the veggies
- Keep a small amount of water at the bottom of your wok (prevents overheating)

Hints:

Stir the pan contents occasionally, and drizzle in just enough water to keep the food from sticking.

For higher fat content in your meal, stir in 1 t. grated coconut during the last few minutes of cooking.

TURKEY OR CHICKEN OR GAME WITH ASPARAGUS, SQUASH AND FRESH GREEN PEAS

½ to 1 c. fresh green peas
2 c. asparagus diced
2 c. squash (acorn or other) diced
1 to 2 c. larger pieces of kale or spinach leaves
2 t. butter
⅓ c. onion or leeks, chopped
¼ t. red pepper (cayenne) or paprika
¼ t. salt, divided, or salt to taste
½ t. coriander
½ t. cumin
¼ t. or a pinch of cinnamon
1 lb. poultry thighs or drums, cut into pieces

- Boil ½ inch of water in a pot fitted with a steamer
- Add green peas and asparagus to steamer, sprinkle with half of the salt
- In 1 or 2 minutes, add the squash and sprinkle with remaining salt
- Steam for 3 to 4 minutes
- Add green leafy vegetables, steam for 1 minute, then remove from heat; do not discard the steamed water
- While the veggies are steaming, melt the butter in a frying pan over medium heat
- Add leeks and seasonings and stir to incorporate
- Add poultry and sauté for two minutes or until no longer pink
- Add a bit of water from the steamed vegetables and continue cooking poultry for no more than 5 minutes
- Pour the finished poultry mixture over the hot vegetables and serve

ROASTED POULTRY DINNER

1 to 2 lbs. chicken, turkey, pheasant or partridge with skin on
1 lb. kohlrabi, turnip, or other vegetables, cut into large pieces/thick slices
3 parsnips cut lengthwise
1 to 3 leeks cut lengthwise
2 beets cut in quarters
3 garlic cloves minced
3 t. olive oil
salt to taste
¼ t. black pepper freshly ground
2 to 3 T. vinegar
1 to 2 T. water
1 T. rosemary dry, coarsely crushed

- Preheat the oven to 425ºF
- In a mixing bowl combine the spices, garlic, salt, water, vinegar and oil
- Gently loosen and separate the skin from the meat to form a pocket
- Rub the herb, vinegar and oil mixture under the skin, spread evenly
- Spread the rest of the mixture over the vegetables
- Place the meat and vegetables on the centre rack in a large roasting pan
- Roast for 20 minutes
- Turn the meat and vegetables and spread the drippings over them
- Continue roasting for 15 minutes
- Turn and baste the drippings over the poultry again and continue roasting till the poultry is cooked and vegetables are at your preferred level of tenderness (10 or more minutes)

Tip:
Use a variety of vegetables of your choice.

PRINCE'S MEATLOAF
The quick and easy comfort food.

1 lb. organic ground bison, ground beef or turkey
½ c. wheat-free bread crumbs
1 egg, slightly beaten
2 T. chili powder
1 large onion, diced
½ T. organic mustard seeds
½ c. grated cheese substitute of your choice

- Preheat oven to 350˚F
- Combine all ingredients in a bowl
- Form into a loaf and place in loaf pan
- Bake for 1 hour; check to ensure center of loaf is fully cooked, not pink

Serve with vegetables, grains and beans.

BEEF OR CHICKEN MARINADE
Sometimes less is more. This marinade can be used to prepare meat for grilling or roasting.

2 T. balsamic vinegar
3 t. fresh tarragon, or 2 t. dried (if you are sensitive to tarragon, try chervil or parsley)
Fresh ground pepper

- Use the above ratio of vinegar to spices to gauge how much you'll need for your meat
- Rub the marinade into the meat
- Place meat in a covered container
- Marinate overnight if possible, or for at least two hours in the fridge

BEEF GOULASH
Old World favourite.

2 to 3 t. butter
1 medium onion, finely diced
⅛ t. pepper
⅛ t. paprika
½ lb. beef cut into bite-size pieces
⅛ t. marjoram
1 to 2 cloves garlic
salt to taste
1 T. non-wheat flour (buckwheat or barley)
Optional additions:
   1 T. radish
   Finely diced vegetables, pickles or olives

- In a fry pan large enough to hold all ingredients, melt butter and sauté onion till golden
- Add the pepper, paprika and beef
- Keep sautéing until the meat colours greyish on the exterior
- Add a bit of water, then the garlic and marjoram
- Cover, reduce heat to simmer, and continue cooking until the meat is tender, about 30 minutes; allow most of the water to evaporate
- Dust on the flour and sauté until the sauce thickens
- If more sauce is wanted, use more onions, garlic, spices, salt and water

If using 'Optional' vegetables, add more water along with the diced vegetables after the sauce has thickened, and cook for a few more minutes until vegetables are tender.

Tip: *Serve over mashed turnip. If you prefer a spicier version, increase the volume of spices, garlic and onion.*

SEASONED, FRIED OR BAKED PORK CHOPS
Although pork meat is delicious, many cultures around the world avoid consuming pork for various reasons. I certainly do not advocate the use of non-organic mass produced pork meat. The best option is organic pork.

2 pork chops
1 to 2 t. butter
salt to taste
¼ t. pepper
Optional:
   ¼ t. paprika
   ¼ t. thyme

If required, tenderize the meat on a cutting board with a wooden mallet. If you do not have a mallet, use the back of a knife or another cutting board.

- Rub the spices into the pork chops and let stand for 10 to 15 minutes.
- Cook in one of the following methods:

Fry
- Melt the butter over medium heat
- Fry the pork chops until both sides are brown; do not overcook

Bake
Preheat oven to 350°F
- Grease baking pan with butter and arrange chops so they are not touching
- Bake for 45 minutes or less
- Salt and season to taste

Serve on a bed of vegetables, grains and beans.

GARLIC-FRIED LAMB
1 lb. lamb, either as chops or bite-size pieces
2 t. butter, or more as needed for frying
2 to 6 cloves garlic, minced
¼ t. pepper
¼ t. salt, or to taste
Optional:
   ¼ t. caraway seeds
   ¼ t. paprika

Continued on next page

Continued from previous page

- Rub the seasonings into the meat and let stand for 10 to 15 minutes
- Melt the butter over medium heat in a frying pan
- Add minced garlic and sauté for 2 minutes
- Add meat and fry until brown; do not overcook
- Add more salt and seasonings if desired
- If you would like a sauce, add in ⅓ cup stock or water before frying is complete and add more seasonings to enhance the flavour
- 1 T. grated sesame seeds, pumpkin seeds or nuts of your choice

Serve with vegetables, grains and beans.

SZEGEDINER GOULASH
½ kg lean pork, cut into cubes
4 T. canola oil
1 large onion, diced
1 T. sweet paprika
¼ t. caraway seeds
1 c. of water
1 jar (800 ml/28 oz) organic sauerkraut, well rinsed
1 T. barley flour

- In a large pot, heat the oil and fry the onions until translucent
- Quickly stir in paprika and add the pork, continually stirring until the meat is coated
- Add caraway seeds and a cup of water
- Reduce the heat and simmer until the meat is nearly done (add water or let some water evaporate so the meat is just covered)
- In a cup, mix barley flour with ¼ cup of water and pour it into the meat mixture
- Mix in the rinsed sauerkraut and add another ½ cup of water
- Let mixture simmer for an additional ½ hour or until soft, adding water as needed

Serve as is or with beans, rye bread or rye bread garlic toast.

Hint: *It is important to rinse the sauerkraut well, otherwise the goulash will be too sharp.*

PORK RIBS
1 rack of ribs, approx. 1 kg
1 T. dried mustard
½ T. tarragon
½ T. thyme
salt to taste
½ c. water

- Cut the ribs into 3 or 4 portions to fit your roasting pan and sprinkle with herbs (generously, if not sensitive to them)
- Add water to the bottom of the pan, cover and roast for about 1½ hrs at 350°F, turning once
- Add a bit more water if required
- Serve with any kind of grain and vegetables of your choice

Optional:
- Add vegetables to the meat and roast them together for the last half hour of cooking
- Add a bit more water to steam the vegetables

PARISIAN FLAVOUR
(MIXTURE OF MEAT SPICES)

1 T. thyme
1 T. chervil
1 T. rosemary
1 T. summer savory
1 t. lavender (optional)
1 t. tarragon
1 t. marjoram
½ t. oregano
½ t. mint
2 bay leaves, crushed

- Mix and store in a tightly sealed container
- Originally intended for lamb, but has been used also for other meats

Note:
Do not use if sensitive to any of the above spices.

CURRIED MEAT WITH VEGETABLES

4 servings of meat, cut into one-inch pieces or into thin strips (beef, pork, lamb, game or poultry)
4 T. butter, or a heavier oil such as rice oil
2 cloves of garlic, crushed
1 large onion, finely chopped
2 c. organic coconut milk
¼ t. of each: ground turmeric, ground cumin, ground coriander seeds
½ to 1 t. curry powder
salt, to taste
2 to 4 c. broccoli and cauliflower, cut into pieces

- Preheat a saucepan on medium heat
- Add butter or heavier oil, and tilt the pan to distribute
- Add garlic, onion, meat and all spices, stir fry for 3 minutes
- Pour in coconut milk and bring to a boil
- Cover and simmer slowly for 30 minutes or until the meat is tender
- When meat is about half done, add the vegetables and finish simmering, stirring occasionally

Serve as is, or with rice, millet or other grains.

BUFFET CABBAGE ROLLS (MEAT AND VEGETARIAN)
Red veggie sauce instead of tomatoes! Save this recipe for when you need to build a batch of food and can endure a slightly trashed kitchen. The results are worth it.

First, start a batch of un-tomato red sauce (recipe in Sauces section).

Meanwhile, the filling (meat version):

1 t. to 1 T. extra virgin olive oil, enough for non-stick sautéing
2 cloves garlic, chopped
1 large onion, chopped
1 to 1.5 lbs. ground meat (beef, bison or turkey)
1 c. uncooked brown rice
½ t. salt
¼ t. pepper

Continued on next page

Continued from previous page

- Pre-cook the brown rice to be half cooked
- Sauté the garlic and onion until the latter is translucent; about 5 minutes
- Set aside to cool slightly
- In a large bowl, combine the raw meat and half-cooked brown rice
- Add the onion mixture, and hand mix until evenly blended

Now the cabbage leaves:

2 heads of cabbage
1 gallon boiling water

- Remove any dirty, torn leaves
- Cut the bottoms off the cabbage heads to eliminate some of the tough stalk and help the leaves release more easily
- Gently remove leaves to avoid tearing until all useable leaves are removed
- Drop leaves three at a time into the boiling water
- Blanch for a minute or two, remove with metal tongs, and start three more leaves
- Arrange the leaves with the stems facing you on a thoroughly clean work surface
- Drop about 1 T. meat/rice/onion mixture onto the bottom third of one leaf, roll the stem end away from you, then fold the left and right sides in, continuing to tuck them in as you roll away from yourself
- This test roll should be snug, with just enough filling. If not, adjust the amount of filling and continue rolling leaves
- Cover the bottom of a stock pot or roaster with some of the red sauce
- As you complete the rolls, place them neatly along the bottom of the pot; layer the rolls only when the bottom is completely covered
- Pour the rest of the red sauce over the rolls and bring them to a simmer
- To create a natural 'steam house' for the rolls, shred all remaining cabbage that wasn't used for rolls and place it overtop the simmering stockpot contents
- Simmer for 2 hours
- Makes about 20 rolls

"I used to feel fatigued and unwell. I tried the conventional route before I was referred to Dr. Kodet. He helped me to achieve a remarkable change in my health. The improvements in my digestive system, energy levels, sleep quality and recovery from a neck injury, were truly dramatic. I even lost weight. One of my daughters received tremendous help from Dr. Kodet during her pregnancy and I am so thankful to have a beautiful healthy granddaughter. All three of my daughters, as well as my granddaughter and myself are Dr. Kodet's patients.

Dr. Kodet is a very caring doctor who takes the time to understand you as a patient and carefully considers all the factors which impact your health. I also appreciate how he seeks to treat the root of each problem as opposed to merely allaying the symptoms."

– Venie Frew

Vegetarian cabbage roll filling:

2 large carrots
2 stalks celery
1 large onion
6 large white button mushrooms
1 t. to 1 T. olive oil, enough for non-stick sautéing
2 c. cooked brown rice
½ t. salt
¼ t. pepper

- All the vegetables can be roughly chopped in a food processor
  with the steel center-mount blade. Chop each type individually
  due to their different textures
- Heat the oil in a skillet large enough to fit the vegetables at
  the bottom of the pan with very little overlap
- Add veggies and sauté for 5 to 7 minutes, or until tender
- Cool mixture slightly, then combine with brown rice
  and seasonings
- Follow rolling and simmering instructions as per the
  meat recipe
- Makes about 20 rolls

CRASH COURSE IN STIR-FRYING

38

Stir-frying is a very fast and efficient way to prepare food if you follow a few simple rules:

- All utensils, including the wok, have to be very clean
- All the ingredients have to be cut, measured and ready to go into the wok before heating the wok; there is no time to do food prep once cooking starts
- Preheat wok to medium or medium/high heat, (electric wok to 350˚F)
- Add 2 T. butter or heavier oil (such as rice oil) and tilt wok to distribute
- Add the ingredients immediately when the oil/butter appears hot; one telltale sign is that the oil/butter will ripple
- Remember, once you add anything to the wok, you are committed to stirring and tossing the contents for the next 1 to 3 minutes
- The seasonings may be mixed into the food before being tossed into the wok, or they may be added to the wok during the initial part of stir-frying
- At the completion of stir-frying, turn the heat off and add a small amount of water, ¼ to ⅓ cup, and put on the lid; this produces a large amount of steam and finishes the cooking
- A cast iron pan or other heavy pan can be substituted for a wok if you do not have one
- If using an electric wok:
  - Preheat the wok to 350ºF
  - Before adding oil and other ingredients, wait until the temperature indicator light is on

STIR–FRY TIMING STRATEGIES

There are numerous opinions on what order various ingredients should be added:

- In general, cooking should start with the harder vegetables first, since they take longer than softer vegetables and meat

- Follow with softer vegetables, timed so that all ingredients are done at the same time; push aside or remove cooked ingredients to prevent overcooking

TIPS:
- *Some chefs keep a bit of water at the bottom of their woks to prevent them from overheating and burning the oil. When the temperature is too high, the excess heat will be dispersed by the evaporating water.*

- *The hotter the oil, the less of it will be absorbed by the food, which is the goal.*

- *Heavier oil, such as rice oil available at some Oriental markets, has a higher burning point.*

  - *Such oil tolerates higher temperatures before it starts burning and producing carcinogenic substances.*

    - *The drawback: Any food item imported from China, or other countries with limited environmental regulations, will likely contain higher amounts of various toxins and carcinogens.*

- *Organic butter, clarified organic butter and animal fats can withstand higher temperatures.*

Note:

There is a greater correlation between heart disease and sugar consumption or use of vegetable oils than there is between heart disease and animal fat consumption.

DO NOT
STIR-FRY WITH:

- *The usually recommended peanut or soy oils.*

- *The 'good' oils, EFAs, (flax and canola oils) high in essential omega-3 fatty acids.*

  - *EFAs have a relatively low burning point and the high heat turns them into unhealthy saturated fats.*

  - *EFAs produce toxic and carcinogenic compounds when heated.*

- *Canned vegetables or anything else canned or previously cooked.*

For better taste:
- Use garlic, onion, nuts and seasonings; make certain the seasonings do not start burning from too little oil/butter

- Marinate meat before stir-frying for a tastier stir-fry

- Stir-fry the vegetables and set aside; <u>clean the wok</u> and add new butter/oil to stir-fry the meat
  - Some people prefer to stir-fry all the ingredients at the same time, adding them according to the cooking time required. Others stir-fry vegetables and meat separately, but they skip cleaning the wok in between. Gourmet cooking may require cooking each ingredient separately, setting each one aside. Meat may take a shorter time to stir-fry than hard vegetables, with the exception of pork. Beef, lamb, duck, turkey, chicken, and seafood usually take less time. Again, undercooked meat is easier to digest than well-done meat

- Evenly cook all ingredients by stir-frying smaller batches and pushing the cooked ingredients aside, rather than attempting to stir-fry a larger amount of food at the same time

- Add butter/oil prior to adding a new batch of food but only as required

- Cook vegetables to a medium firmness; those with weak digestive systems will likely need to overcook them

TIME REQUIRED FOR STIR-FRYING

Meat: depending on the size of pieces and kind of meat, cooking time will range from:

- 1 to 3 minutes for average bite-size pieces
- Up to 5 minutes for one-inch thick slices of meat

Vegetables also take 1 to 3 minutes:

- Hard vegetables such as kohlrabi, cauliflower, broccoli, carrots, beets and rutabaga take longer to cook
- Radishes such as daikon or turnip may take less time
- Leafy vegetables take barely a minute

Eggs take less than 2 minutes:

- Easier to boil or poach in a wok than in other cookware
- A wok will also facilitate other forms of cooking eggs, such as scrambling
- Use lower temperatures than for meat or hard vegetables
- The simplest, fastest method is to add the eggs at the very end of stir-frying

Fresh green peas in pods, fresh white or yellow beans:

- Takes about 5 minutes when cut up into small quarter-inch pieces

- Although it may seem complex at the first glance, stir-frying is a very easy form of cooking. It allows us to prepare a complete, truly healthy and tasty meal in minutes.

- It is also considered more effective in destroying microbial agents and preserving nutritional values than some other cooking methods.

- Another advantage is that you do not need to follow elaborate recipes or shop for special ingredients. Just select a variety of vegetables, seasonings and a source of protein, chop everything up, throw it into a preheated, oiled/buttered wok and stir.

"Dr. Kodet's care and knowledge have contributed significantly to the state of my current health, including continued remission from two separate cancers. His knowledge base is expansive, encompassing a complete program of naturopathy, homeopathy, nutrition, exercise and emotional well-being. In a high-tech world where social chaos and economic instability are the norm, it is refreshing to see that the tried and true ways still play a key role in maintaining health and balance. Dr. Kodet is an expert in bringing these methodologies to the layperson in a concise, empathetic and effective way."

– Rita Egizii

1997 Canadian Woman Entrepreneur of the Year (Alberta)

2006 Global Television Woman of Vision

CRASH COURSE IN BRAISING

There are various interpretations on what constitutes braising. Purists define it as cooking without any oil or fat, as follows:

- Preheat skillet or a thick-bottomed pot
- Add enough water to cover the bottom
- At high heat, add the ingredients, such as larger pieces of meat, fish, poultry, and vegetables
- Stir, if required, and add more water to prevent scorching (the meat should not be fully submerged)
- Add a splash of wine, vinegar or lemon juice (something acidic)
- Lower the heat, cover, and continue cooking until tender, stirring occasionally if required
- Add additional ingredients, such as seasonings or those required to make sauce or gravy
- Stir occasionally if required, and cook for several hours until tender
- If desired, add healthy oils when done (usually flax or hemp seed oils)

Hint: *Allow 2 to 4 hours, or even overnight, for braising food.*

Gourmet braising advocates turning up the heat to brown all ingredients <u>before</u> adding wine, lemon juice or vinegar. From there:

- Partially cover the meat with water
- Lower heat, cover with a tight-fitting lid and continue cooking
- Add additional ingredients, such as seasonings or those required to make sauce or gravy
- Stir occasionally if required, and cook for several hours until tender

The primary advantages of this type of cooking are:

- Reduction of fat damage
- Capacity to tenderize and enhance flavour of tougher meats (such as cheaper cuts, tendons, etc.)
  - Some cooks use a slow cooker for this purpose; this may be a more practical approach
- One-dish cooking

ORGAN MEATS

Historically, all cultures around the world considered meat from internal organs to be a delicacy since it is of superior quality to muscle meat. Increasingly, modern research is supporting this opinion. Many culinary delicacies around the world are made from internal organs.

Oriental medicine advocates consuming internal organs as part of its treatment protocols. For example, Chinese medicine advises us to eat liver or kidneys if our liver or kidneys are deficient or diseased.

By the way, we modern North Americans are doing the same thing without even realizing it. Many of our supplements are made from internal organs; some of them are hardly processed or cooked. And remember that naturopathic physicians prescribe desiccated liver, adrenals, kidney and other organ preparations or extracts daily.

NOTE:
ALL INTERNAL ORGANS MUST COME FROM VERIFIABLY ORGANIC SOURCES. OTHERWISE, DO NOT USE THEM!

SIMPLE GOURMET CHICKEN OR GAME BIRD LIVERS
2 to 4 bird livers
¼ t. pepper
¼ t. paprika
1 to 2 cloves garlic
2 to 3 t. butter
Salt, to taste, AFTER liver is cooked.

Tip:
Heart can be prepared the same way as any muscle meat.

* Rub liver with pepper and paprika
* Preheat frying pan and melt the butter over medium-high heat
* Briefly stir-fry garlic in butter to enhance flavour, and leave in the pan
* Add the liver and fry for about a minute on each side
* The liver should be crisp on the outside and tender on the inside
  * If you prefer liver more thoroughly cooked inside, fry it at a lower heat for longer
  * The gourmet approach requires higher heat and short cooking times to create the delicious crispness on the outside with a tender inside; it also retains more flavour and nutrients
* Adjust seasonings if required

NOTE:
NEVER SALT LIVER OR KIDNEYS DURING COOKING. IT WILL MAKE THEM TOUGH!

Serve as you would any other meat.

HEART

In general, cultures that consider heart meat a delicacy, tend to use special recipes to prepare it.

In my experience, there is no need for special recipes. Use the same recipes as for muscle meat. Make a beef heart just like a beef steak, or stir-fry chicken hearts, the same way as any chicken meat. Try it and you will not be disappointed.

Note:

An alternative to washing the kidneys is boil them briefly and discard the water.

HAZELNUT CHICKEN LIVER DELICACY

2 to 4 bird livers
¼ to ½ c. chopped hazelnuts
¼ to ½ c. chopped green onions
2 to 3 t. butter
Salt, to taste, AFTER liver is cooked.

- Preheat frying pan and melt the butter over medium-high heat
- Briefly stir-fry onions and hazelnuts and leave in the pan
- Add the liver and fry for about a minute on each side
- The liver should be crisp on the outside and tender on the inside
  - If you prefer liver more thoroughly cooked inside, fry it at a lower heat for longer
  - The gourmet approach requires higher heat and short cooking times to create the delicious crispness on the outside with a tender inside; it also retains more flavour and nutrients
- Adjust seasonings if required (pepper, paprika)

Serve as you would any other meat.

QUICK-FRIED KIDNEYS

1 lb. kidneys, cut into pieces as desired
2 to 3 t. butter
¼ to ½ t. pepper
¼ to ½ t. caraway seeds
Optional: 1 t. barley flour
Salt to taste, AFTER kidneys are cooked

- Cut the kidneys into thin strips or steakettes; cut off fat and discard
- Wash the pieces well and soak the kidneys in water overnight or for several hours, changing the water a few times
- In a strainer, gently squeeze the water out of the meat by applying pressure with your hand; repeat washing and squeezing several times
- Preheat frying pan and melt the butter
- Place kidneys in frying pan and season with pepper and caraway
- Stir or turn pieces occasionally for even browning
- **Option:** When kidneys are nearly done, sprinkle the flour over them and briefly stir-fry until fully cooked
- Kidneys should be fully cooked in about 5 minutes
- Add salt to taste

Serve with rye bread or other grains, beans and vegetables.

SAUTÉED KIDNEYS

1 medium onion, chopped
2 cloves garlic
1 lb. kidneys, cut into pieces as desired
2 to 3 t. butter
¼ to ½ t. pepper
¼ to ½ t. caraway seeds
1 T. barley or buckwheat flour
Salt to taste, AFTER kidneys are cooked

- Cut the kidneys into bite-size pieces and cut off fat and discard
- Wash the pieces well and soak the kidneys in water overnight or for several hours, changing the water a few times
- In a strainer, gently squeeze the water out of the meat by applying pressure with your hand; repeat washing and squeezing several times
- Preheat frying pan and melt the butter
- Add the chopped onions and garlic and sauté for about 3 minutes or until translucent
- Place kidneys in fry pan and season with pepper and caraway
- Stir or turn pieces occasionally for even browning; this should only take a minute or two
- Blend 1 to 2 T. of buckwheat flour or barley flour in ½ to 1 cup of water and slowly add to pan while stirring
- Add more seasonings, to taste
- Heat until bubbling and continue to cook and stir for a few more minutes
- Add more water gradually, if required to keep gravy at desired consistency
- Kidneys should be fully cooked with about 5 minutes of total heat exposure
- Add salt to taste only after the kidneys are done

" I used to be sceptical of any alternative/naturopathic medicine but, after I saw what Dr. Kodet did for my daughter I also became his patient. I suffered a miscarriage in the spring of 2006. I wanted to have another child and, being 39, felt I needed to do something to prevent any further miscarriages and to improve my capacity to conceive and deliver a healthy child. Dr. Kodet put me on his special diet and also treated me with manual visceral manipulation, herbs, specific supplements, and exercises to improve fertility and pregnancy. In a few months I became pregnant again. My pregnancy was healthy and, in the fall of 2007, I gave birth to a healthy baby boy. I am very happy with Dr. Kodet's treatments and my family's health. "

– Marta Vajsablova

BASIC FISH (TROUT, SALMON OR OTHER FISH)
Sometimes less is more, especially with a very fresh trout. This recipe may also be used with other fish.

1 trout
2 t. butter
salt to taste
Optional: black pepper to taste
lemon juice to taste (if not aggravating)
1 clove garlic

* Wash the fish, pat dry
* Bake or fry in butter or poach and top with butter when done
* When almost done, season with salt, pepper and lemon juice to taste
* If the thickest part of the flesh flakes with a fork, it is done; do not overcook

FISH FOR THE FUSSIES
Filet of sole or pollock are the fish of choice for the uninitiated. They're mild, tender and cook quickly.

oil for the pan
1 to 2 t. (clarified) organic butter or extra virgin olive oil
Fish fillets (up to ½ lb. per child, up to 1 lb. per adult)
salt and pepper
¼ c. water

* Preheat oven to 350°F
* Lightly oil a baking pan that's about 1.5 inch deep
* Arrange fillets so they are not touching
* Dot each fish piece with butter, or drizzle with the olive oil
* Season to your liking
* Place the pan of fish on the top rack of the oven so that you may broil it for the last minute or so if desired
* Bake about 10 minutes, and broil only long enough to slightly brown
* Do not overcook, or it will be tough

CAUTION:
MANY OF US HAVE ADVERSE REACTIONS TO FISH OR TO THE MERCURY THAT'S IN THE FISH.

Tips:
Undercook fish rather than overcook.

To test for doneness, press the thickest part of the fish with your finger. It should feel firm. Or, if the thickest part flakes with a fork, it's ready.

STEAMED FISH (TROUT, SALMON OR OTHER FISH) WITH GREENS

1 lb. fish steaks
1 t. fresh ginger root finely chopped
1 t. dill chopped fresh or dried
2 small or medium scallions
1 c. watercress or other green leafy vegetables
1 c. fresh bean sprouts
1 c. beet tops
Optional:
2 T. olive, flax seed or other oil
½ t. vinegar or 1 t. lemon juice
1 small clove of garlic
(avoid if sensitive to it)
pinch of salt
pinch of black pepper ground

* Mix dill, ginger, vinegar or lemon juice, salt, pepper and rub it into the fish steaks
* Let sit for 20 min
* Put ½ to ¾ inches of water into a steamer and bring to a boil
* Place the fish steaks on the steamer
* Place the lid on and adjust the heat to maintain boiling temperature
* Steam for 5 to 10 minutes depending on the thickness of the fish
* Remove the fish and place on a heated plate
* Gradually add the vegetables into the steamer (beet tops first and softer watercress with bean sprouts later)
* **Optional:** Crush a clove of garlic, mix with the oil and drizzle over the vegetables prior to serving.

SEASONED FISH

This savory version is delicious with many fish favourites.

1 fish of your choice
⅛ to ¼ t. caraway seeds
¼ to ½ t. freshly chopped parsley
¼ to ½ t. finely minced garlic
½ t. lemon juice
salt to taste
Optional: 1 t. to 1 T. non-wheat flour (barley, buckwheat)

* If using flour, coat the fish in the flour
* Mix any or all of the above spices, along with lemon juice into the butter
* Spread the seasoned butter onto the fish
* Bake or fry just until done

To test for doneness, press the thickest part of the fish with your finger. It should feel firm. Or, if the thickest part flakes with a fork, it's ready.

Serve with the butter it was cooked in; add salt and lemon juice to taste. Goes well with rice, millet and vegetable dishes.

IN GENERAL, HEATED LIME AND LEMON JUICE BECOME LESS IRRITATING. IF NOT CERTAIN ABOUT LEMON JUICE AVOID IT OR ADD IT BEFORE COOKING.

*BUTTERFLYING A FISH
Cut the inside of the spine lengthwise deep enough to allow splaying the fish but not separating the skin.

FRIED WHITEFISH WITH SOUTHERN GREEN SAUCE

1 lb. whitefish
1 t. finely chopped cilantro
1 t. finely chopped parsley
1 t. finely chopped dill
¼ t. pepper
1 to 2 cloves garlic
½ to 1 t. horseradish
2 t. butter
salt, to taste

- Melt butter in a frying pan over medium heat
- Add the seasonings and sauté to soften them
- Place filets in the seasoned butter and fry on both sides until almost done
- Serve with a grain (rice, millet, buckwheat) plus vegetables and legumes
- Pour the remaining seasoned pan butter over the filets and the other foods and serve

BAKED TROUT OR SALMON ON TOP OF VEGETABLES

1 trout (1 lb.) cut in half lengthwise (butterflying*) or use two salmon filets (½ lb. each) with the skin
½ lb. rutabaga cut into long thin strips
½ lb. turnip cut into long thin strips
½ lb. leeks cut into long thin strips
¼ to ⅓ t. fresh dill chopped
2 garlic cloves minced (optional)
2 T. vinegar or lemon juice
2 t. olive oil
¼ t. black pepper freshly ground
¼ t. salt

- Preheat the oven to 400˚F
- In a small dish, combine spices, salt, garlic, vinegar or lemon juice
- Spread and press half of the spices into the exposed fish meat
- Press both spiced sides of the trout or fish filet together leaving the skin on the outside
- Spread the vegetables in the roasting pan
- Mix the oil into the mixture of spices
- Drizzle the oil over the vegetables
- Place the fish on the top of the vegetables, keeping the spiced sides together
- Cover with a lid and bake for 15 minutes
- Stir the vegetables, flip the fish
- Continue baking it for an additional 15 minutes or until the fish is tender
- Separate the fillets and drizzle the pan juices over the fillets

"*My seven-year-old son was diagnosed by a pediatrician as ADD in late 2008. His inability to stay focused on tasks was greatly affecting his schoolwork and home life. Most doctors I saw advised medications. I was also advised of alternate treatments such as naturopathic remedies or diet changes.*

As to the rest of my family, several of us, including myself, suffer from food and environmental allergies ranging from mild to severe and so I experienced first hand the impact a diet can have on one's general health. With my regular naturopathic doctor no longer practicing in Calgary I went online to find someone who had success with children and ADD. This is how I found Dr. Kodet.

After a thorough exam and a whole lot of questions, Dr Kodet advised putting him on an organic diet consisting of fresh cooked foods served on a rotation basis. This also involved eliminating known foods that cause allergic reactions in some people. Finally, through a simple strength test he added some naturopathic remedies to aid in the elimination of toxins while building up the immune system. With regular visits in the first month I admit the results were not immediate. But during the second month, I could see that my son was finding it easier to concentrate on a single task at a time and was staying interested. By the third month, he was able to perform multiple tasks without being distracted. His teacher commented during a parent teacher interview that he didn't seem to have ADD. Today, he is one of the top readers in his class and also good at math!

I've come to understand more fully the implications of a healthy diet. There have been occasions when in a hurry, I've given my son a processed or sugary food. I've observed his level of concentration drop noticeably. Dr. Kodet's cookbook is a practical manifestation of his generous care and his utmost commitment to his patients."

– Rae-Lene Berube

THE FORGOTTEN INGREDIENT: FUN

42

HERE ARE SOME FUN IDEAS TO MAKE HEATHY FOODS EVEN MORE APPEALING.

1. Use a mould:
   * Place cooked grain (rice, millet, etc.) into an egg-poaching cup, coffee cup or soup bowl
   * Press firmly, and invert a nicely formed shape onto each plate.
   * Beans, sauces, vegetables or other ingredients can be arranged around the form

2. Try wraps and pancakes – the trendy alternative to sandwiches

3. Stack seasoned beans or vegetables on top of pancakes, breads or crêpes

4. Serve dip platters:
   * Wheat-free breads, crackers, large pieces of hard steamed veggies, or even cooked and cubed meat can be used to dip into a bean/vegetable spread. Use a fork or toothpick for pieces that are too small to hold between your fingers
   * Roll up lightly cooked, softer leafy vegetables lengthwise, secure with a toothpick and use for dipping

5. Enjoy your good china – vegetables or beans buttered, dusted with herbs and presented in a beautiful bowl elevate food above the everyday standard

6. Option for Kebabs: Meats, veggies, and even a bit of fruit, can be cooked and served on the same skewer

7. Use your Fondue: Whip one up the same as you always would, only with healthier ingredients

8. Thick soups or stew can be served in a small homemade loaf of bread. Just hollow out the inside of an appropriately shaped non-wheat loaf, butter it, place it in a bowl or on a dish for support, and ladle in the soup or stew

9. Cut cooked eggs in half instead of peeling them. Let children eat the eggs from their shells with a small spoon

10. Use avocado or egg shells, or hollowed out squash to serve food

11. Involve your children in cooking to increase the likelihood of them eating the results

MEDICINAL HERBS IN THE KITCHEN

43

Culinary herbs can do much more than enhance palatability, aroma and appearance of our foods. Many of them also improve our digestion, absorption, elimination, immune system and other aspects of our health. They can act synergistically with other herbs or singularly to produce various healing effects. Although herbs can act in many ways, I will note only some of their more relevant benefits. Please keep in mind that herbs may affect people differently. Some of us who are more sensitive may react to them more vigorously or even adversely.

The following herbs are commonly used in Western cuisine and have a long track record of medicinal use. As a part of our diet, culinary herbs can significantly assist in improving our general health, well-being and performance. In addition, they can also play an important supportive role in recovery from a variety of illnesses. This includes severe chronic illnesses.

The information provided here will help anyone from expert to beginner to use herbs safely and effectively.

Please keep in mind: No matter how mild and beneficial a herb, there is always someone who will react to it adversely.

HERB AND SPICE HOT LIST

Many cooking herbs have medicinal attributes. Please don't limit your use of herbs to this general list; in fact, I encourage everyone to experiment with, learn about, and add other culinary and medicinal herbs to their food.

■ ALLSPICE *(Pimenta officionalis)*

Allspice contains eugenol, which is the active ingredient responsible for reducing dental pain. Eugenol is also found in clove oil and allspice oil. Allspice has been used externally as an oil, a poultice, a plaster and in the bath to reduce muscle and joint pain, including arthritic pain and neuralgia.

However, we are more interested in its capacity to improve the production of digestive enzymes, reduce indigestion, diarrhea, intestinal gas and bloating.

■ ANISE *(Pimpinella anisum)*

This is one of the herbs which our ancestors used to pay taxes. At another time, anise was subjected to a special sales tax to help pay for the repair of London's bridges. Currently, our governmental agencies prefer to collect our money as opposed to our anise.

Nonetheless, most of us still use anise as an aromatic and culinary herb. It promotes and stimulates digestion and reduces cramps and gas. Anise has been one of the preferred herbs to use in digestive formulas for infants, specifically for infantile colic. Hippocrates, the father of Western natural medicine, used it to clear mucus from the respiratory system.

Regarding its mild estrogenic activity, anise is one of the herbs used to relieve menopausal discomfort. In addition, it is a galactagogue (milk-flow promoting herb) that can also relieve morning sickness.

Other uses are: a breath freshener (just chew the tiny seeds), a replacement for licorice in commercial preparations and a component of lozenges, cough remedies, liquors and candies.

■ BASIL *(Ocimum basilicum/sanctum)*

Basil is one of the herbs that has been used for almost any ailment. This might be due to basil being an immune stimulant and an anti-spasmodic that has numerous beneficial actions on the digestive system. Some of those actions are: anti-parasitic, anti-vermifuge (acts against worms), demulcent (soothing), anti-spasmodic, appetite stimulant, bile and milk-flow promoter, plus intestinal pain and vomiting reliever. Oriental medicine uses it to treat kidney, blood and stomach problems.

Due to its antibacterial action, it has been used topically to treat acne.

In many cultures, basil is considered a highly spiritual herb. It is used to guard against anger, hostility and headaches; it's supposed to offer protection to the user, repelling evil spirits while attracting love and faithfulness. If your life seems to be low on love, start cooking with basil and see what transpires.

■ BAY LEAF *(laurel, sweet bay, green bay)*

In the old days, bay leaf was used for virtually every ailment. Today, it continues to be used for arthritis, and to induce menstruation and labour. Modern applications also exploit its soothing and sedating effects. Since it also has a mild antibacterial and antifungal effect, do not hesitate to use it for disinfecting minor wounds.

■ BLACK PEPPER *(Piper nigrum)*

In general, the effects of this spice are similar to that of red pepper, but surprisingly, black pepper is somewhat more aggressive. Sensitive people may find it over-stimulating or even stomach burning. In addition, it is an irritating expectorant. Black pepper tones digestion and has carminative effects (reduces gas, bloating and pain).

■ CARAWAY SEEDS *(Carum carvi)*

On one hand, caraway is widely known for its aroma and mildly spicy flavour. On the other hand, it has almost been forgotten as one of our oldest medicinal herbs. From the times of the Greek empire to the present, caraway has been used to stimulate digestion, soothe the gastro-intestinal tract and help to relieve spasms, gas and infantile colic. In addition, it helps with detoxification because it stimulates conjugation of glutathione.

Caraway seeds have been used to relax the uterus to relieve menstrual cramps, improve amenorrhea (no menstruation) and to stimulate the production of milk in nursing mothers.

It has been prescribed, in tea form, as an expectorant to clear up chest congestion and colds.

Again, keep in mind that even the least allergenic and irritating herb or food can irritate someone.

■ CARDAMOM *(Elletaria cardamomum)*

Mildly stimulating, these seeds are used to enhance aroma, improve appetite, reduce stomach pain and facilitate production and release of gas.

■ CAYENNE, RED PEPPER OR CHILI PEPPER *(Capsicum frutescens)*

This is one of the spices that doesn't get enough credit for its benefits. Red pepper is primarily a warming and stimulating herb. It improves digestion by increasing the production of hydrochloric acid, digestive juices and intestinal movement. It also warms up and tones the stomach.

Its systemic effects include increased circulation, bodily heat production, sweating and expectoration. As you might know from flu season, expectorant herbs help you eliminate secretions from your respiratory system.

Apart from its antimicrobial and anti-inflammatory functions, red pepper is also a mild diuretic with a demulcent (soothing) and restorative effect. Red pepper promotes adrenal gland activity and enhances the actions of other herbs. Clearly, this spice is excellent for those who feel cold, sluggish, weak and depleted.

Red pepper can be used externally to reduce arthritic, nerve and other pains. The pain reduction is based on its warming effect and depletion of substance 'P', the neurotransmitter polypeptide which transmits pain.

■ CHAMOMILE *(Matrica chamomila)*

This herb was the primary choice of my grandmother and her contemporaries for treating infantile colic. While many of today's sensitive patients react to chamomile in herbal or tea form, they may tolerate it in a tincture form. Regardless, I usually do not 'irritate the devil' and use a different herb with similar benefits for these patients.

Chamomile is a wonderful and versatile herb with a fabulous aroma. Chamomile used to be one of the primary herbs for the digestive system, including stomach ulcer treatment. Research has confirmed that chamomile relaxes the digestive tract just as well as the opium-based drug papaverine.

Chamomile's antispasmodic properties relax or reduce menstrual cramps and promote the onset of menstruation.

Our ancestors considered it a very effective calming herb, and they were correct. Chamomile tends to calm an over-reactive or over-irritated central nervous system. One of my instructors at naturopathic medical school stated that chamomile works well for children "who just scream their heads off". This herb is also used to relieve anxiety, either as a tea, tincture, or in a hot bath. Again, when using it with children or highly sensitive patients, check for allergic reactions.

Chamomile is also a good remedy for external wounds when used as a compress, poultice, or more often, as a bath. Apart from the pleasant aroma and its ability to induce a warm, soothing feeling, patients also benefit from its anti-candidal, antimicrobial effect and a faster rate of healing.

■ CELERY *(Apium graveolans)*

Our ancestors correctly identified celery seed as a highly effective diuretic. In fact, experimental evidence confirms its effectiveness in reducing high blood pressure and improving congestive heart failure. For the same reason, celery seeds have been used to combat water retention and aid weight loss.

Celery seed is known to have sedative effects, which lead to its use for anxiety, nervousness and insomnia. They have been also used to promote or induce menstruation, cleanse the skin and improve appetite and digestion. Since we tend to criminalize herbs more than pharmaceutical preparations, I have to advise you to be cautious if you decide to use celery seeds during pregnancy.

I should not neglect this herb's place in reducing symptoms of gout, rheumatic conditions and various pulmonary illnesses such as bronchitis. Studies have also confirmed celery seed's capacity to improve diabetes by reducing blood sugar.

Since it contains psoralen, some people considered using celery seed to treat psoriasis and T-cell lymphoma. I would not hesitate to use celery seed for these conditions, but only in conjunction with other herbs and natural therapies.

Oil extract from celery roots has been used to recover sexual potency depleted by illness.

■ CINNAMON (Cinnamomum saigonum or Cinnamomum zeylanicum)

Cinnamon is a warming, stimulating, drying spice. Since cinnamon helps to stop bleeding, it was traditionally used to control obstetric bleeding. Our ancestors also used it to relieve menstruation abnormalities, fever, colds, flus, nausea, vomiting and infant colic.

Cinnamon is a digestive system stimulant to the point of being a laxative in large doses. On the other hand, since it is a drying and corrective spice, it can treat diarrhea and prevent cramping produced by irritant laxatives. It also reduces, gas, bloating and related pain.

These days, cinnamon is a common ingredient in toothpaste. Due to its germicidal or antiseptic capacities, cinnamon can be used topically. If used externally, cinnamon has the capacity to prevent the spread of E.coli and Candida albicans infections.

Cinnamon can be applied directly onto the skin for cuts and scrapes. If your child is highly sensitive, try it first on a small area of unbroken skin. Or even better, the more sensitive parent can test it on himself/herself before trying it on the child. Test cinnamon prior to requiring it so that you'll know the reaction before an urgent need arises.

■ CLOVES (Caryophylum aromaticus or Szygium aromaticum)

Cloves are famous for their pain-reducing capacity. Dentists used clove oil to reduce dental pain and to disinfect the surgical site in the mouth. Laypeople who didn't have clove oil chewed a whole clove or placed it against the painful area in the mouth. It is also an antimicrobial, antiviral, antifungal and antiparasitic herb. It is indicated in the treatment of digestive disorders, diarrhea and vomiting. In addition, it is one of the most effective breath fresheners and is high in antioxidants. Do not overdo it with cloves – they can be harmful in high doses.

■ COFFEE (Coffea arabica)

Loved by most, adored by many (beverage producers are even starting to add it to beer!). Given its commercial appeal, we will see a lot of misinformation about the wonders of the coffee bean supported in various studies.

The herb coffea, if used appropriately, can be very beneficial. It is used to improve the symptoms of asthma, headaches, fever/flu, jet-lag and encourages weight loss. It is a central nervous system stimulant, counteracts the sedative effects of antihistamines, and increases stamina.

Perpetual long-term consumption may lead to the development of a condition called 'Caffeinism'. This condition produces the same symptoms as anxiety neurosis: nervousness, irritability, chronic muscle tension, insomnia, heart palpitation, diarrhea, heartburn and stomach upset. In addition, it produces throbbing headaches, increased release of hydrochloric acid, high blood pressure, elevated cholesterol levels and risk of heart attack.

Increased consumption of coffee is linked to fibrocystic breast changes. As well, it is considered a factor in increased PMS, reduced capacity to absorb iron and reduced capacity to conceive.

■ CORIANDER OR CILANTRO
(Coriandrum sativum)
Although it calms digestion, coriander is not considered as soothing as caraway or some other digestive herbs. Nonetheless, it has been added to the meals of those suffering from digestive and gynecological disorders including infantile colic or amenorrhea. It also has the potential to lower blood sugar.

Because of its antimicrobial and antifungal properties, coriander can be used as a meat preservative.

Although patients can adversely react to anything, I would expect fewer adverse reactions to coriander than to caraway seeds. In fact, many herbal texts recommend coriander for the treatment of asthma. One of the reasons: in order to improve asthma, you have to improve digestion.)

You can treat topical wounds with coriander thanks to its antimicrobial, antiviral and antifungal properties; some herbalists also list it as an anti-inflammatory.

Coriander is an ingredient in many natural deodorants because it smells pleasant and is antimicrobial. It is also used for bad breath, usually as a tea.

■ DILL (Antheum graveolense)
Dill is used in many cuisines for its highly aromatic, flavourful qualities and can be seen in table decorations or plate garnishes. Dill is one of the most effective herbs to eliminate bad breath.

From a medicinal perspective, it promotes appetite, digestion, reduces sour taste, decreases intestinal gas and helps to expel trapped gas. Furthermore, it inhibits the growth of several pathogenic bacteria in the digestive and urinary tracts. To prevent reoccurrence of bacterial overgrowth in these tissues, you may add dill to your cooking, drink it as a tea, or even use it in your bath. Since it is very mild and soothing for the intestinal system, I often recommend it as one of the herbs for digestive disorders in children. Herbalists prescribe dill for various disorders including insufficient milk production. Dill also helps with detoxification for the same reasons as caraway seeds.

Egyptians, Romans, Greeks, Vikings and other early Europeans used dill for various purposes, but primarily as a food preservative and as a soothing digestive herb.

■ FENNEL (Foeniculum vulgare)
Fennel is used to relieve stomach and intestinal pain, gas and spasms. Similar to many aromatic herbs, it also improves appetite.

In women's health, low doses relax the uterus while higher doses stimulate it. Fennel has been used to reduce menstrual discomfort and as a galactagogue (milk-flow promoting herb).

Fennel's mildly estrogenic effect leads some herbalists to prescribe it as a complementary treatment for prostate cancer. My word of caution is, competent natural treatment of prostate cancer requires more than fennel.

■ GARLIC *(Allium sativum)*

From a medicinal perspective, garlic is the most versatile of all medicinal herbs. In fact, on exams at naturopathic medical school, we were not allowed to use garlic in our answers. The reason is that garlic can be used as a supportive herb in the vast majority of illnesses (provided the patient was not allergic or sensitive to it).

Historically, various cultures treasured garlic as one of the sacred herbs. For example, Egyptians swore oaths on garlic as we do on the Bible or other religious texts, when in court. When going to war, Cossacks were told to bring their weapons plus bacon or garlic.

Garlic is known for its antimicrobial, antifungal, antiviral and anti-protozoal properties. The term 'Russian Penicillin', originated from garlic's capacity to act as a broad-spectrum antibiotic on infected wounds. Historically it was also used in the treatment of a variety of infections, including fungal infections (athlete's foot, vaginitis, etc.).

It is a warming herb that has been commonly used in the treatment and prevention of respiratory illnesses such as flu and bronchitis.

Less known is its application in the treatment and prevention of cardiac conditions. Garlic has been used to improve blood thinning and reduce blood pressure, blood lipids and glucose.

As with many other herbs, garlic has been used in the prevention and treatment of various cancers. Probably the most popularized has been its use in the treatment of stomach cancer. My opinion is that successful treatment of cancer requires more than garlic.

There are various recommendations on how to handle the infamous odour of garlic. You can reduce it by eating parsley, fennel or fenugreek, to mention a few ideas. When I eat raw garlic, I usually prefer to phone my friends rather than see them in person. This improves my chances of keeping my friends longer.

In the genus *Allium*, garlic is considered the most effective and most researched. Other members of this genus are onions, leeks, scallions (green onions) and chives, which all have similar healing properties. However, they are not as powerful and versatile as the mighty garlic.

Unfortunately, many people have sensitivity to garlic, onions and other members of this family, so exercise some caution until you are sure of your tolerance.

■ GINGER *(Zingiber officionalis)*

Ginger is one of the major digestive herbs in terms of its versatility and effectiveness. Its impact on the whole digestive system is clearly impressive. It increases the flow of saliva (digestion starts in the mouth) as well as the amount of hydrochloric acid and digestive juices in the stomach. It also has a demulcent (soothing) effect. This results in improving digestive capacities, reducing gas, bloating, indigestion and intestinal cramps. Hydrochloric acid breaks down the proteins and stimulates production of digestive juices. Usually it is a lack of hydrochloric acid that causes us to feel that our food is sitting heavy in our stomachs.

If your child's skin surface feels cool, consider using ginger as a spice when cooking or as a tea. Ginger is warming and can warm up even very weak, chilly and sluggish patients. Since it is an expectorant and sweat-promoting herb, it has been used to fight acute colds and influenza infections.

Ginger is an effective herb used to prevent or reduce motion sickness, morning sickness and nausea resulting from chemotherapy. In fact, it works better for nausea than Dramamine, a conventional medication. In addition, it is side-effect free and does not lead to depletion of micronutrients. In fact, ginger improves digestion and absorption of nutrients.

Many culinary herbs have an antispasmodic action with an affinity for the gastrointestinal and reproductive systems. Ginger is one of them and has been effectively used to relieve menstrual cramps and infrequent menstruation (oligomenorrhea).

Our ancestors knew that ginger reduced swelling, stiffness and pain while improving the mobility of arthritic joints. This may be the reason why older texts list it as an anti-inflammatory herb and advocate its use in the treatment of arthritis.

Since ginger reduces cholesterol, blood pressure and clotting, it is often added into protocols directed to prevent and treat heart disease and stroke.

Oriental medicine often uses ginger for external applications. Such applications may involve anything from reduction of pain, inflammation, fever and tumors. (Please, do not try self-treatment for tumors. Treatment of cancer is not for beginners. You have to know exactly how to do it – otherwise, you might promote cancer growth instead of reducing it.)

Some of us can develop sensitivities or allergies to almost any herb, food or medication. Highly sensitive people may react to a particular substance even if the quantity consumed is very, very small. Ginger is a herb as well as a food, so it is not excluded from this caution.

Patients who have very sensitive digestive systems, gastro-esophageal reflux or a history of miscarriages may find ginger overly stimulating. The good news is that their reaction to this herb is usually proportional to the amount they consume. Nonetheless, an overwhelming majority of people benefit from ginger when it is used in small quantities, such as the amounts used in cooking.

■ HOPS *(Humulus lupulus)*

It is easy to see why some of us love to consume this herb in higher than medicinal quantities and for other than medicinal reasons. Hops promote the production of bile which helps us to detoxify and emulsify (digest) fats. It is also a mild laxative, sedative and improves appetite.

I use hops as a sleep inducer. All of the above may explain why Europeans intuitively liked to drink their beer after a dinner or a Sunday meal. Regardless, I think it was the taste more than the health concerns that caused the Czechs to resist selling their breweries to foreign investors. They also have an official political party called Beer Party and a famous national saying: "Any government that increases the price of beer must fall".

Hops have been used to relieve dysmenorrhea (painful menstruation) and insomnia of nervous origin. I would definitely not recommend using beer for these purposes – instead, use a hops tea.

However, not all of this herb's actions are beneficial and pleasing. For example, hops have significant phyto-estrogenic effects, meaning it is unlikely that a six-pack of beer would help you develop a distinct six-pack of abdominal muscles. In fact, the estrogenic effect promotes the development of breasts and a lovelier, more rounded feminine appeal in men, and menstrual abnormalities in women. This contradicts what the beer commercials want us to believe.

So, those of us who intend to use it for medicinal or other purposes should use it as a tea. Avoid beer with nasty additives and keep in mind that sometimes less is more.

■ LICORICE (Glycerrhiza glabra)

Licorice is sixty times sweeter than sugar, yet it is considered glucose balancing. The sweetness and the unique pleasant taste it provides make it a healthy substitute for sugar. Reduced consumption of sugar helps to decrease our risks of diabetes, tooth decay, excessive fatty deposits, cardiovascular conditions and other degenerative diseases.

Licorice has a demulcent (soothing) effect on our sysems and anti-inflammatory capacities. It became quite famous because of its effectiveness in treating peptic ulcers; an Irish study confirmed that licorice worked better than the conventional medication Tagament (also known as a Cimetidine). The added advantage is that this herb does not have the side-effect of candida overgrowth.

Many preparations for adrenal weakness contain licorice. Adrenals are the stress glands. The validity of such use is supported by the fact that licorice contains cortisone-like constituents; adrenals produce cortisol.

Licorice has also been used to balance the levels of progesterone and estrogen. Patients suffering from constipation found relief when using this herb, because it can produce a laxative effect when required. It is also known for an antiviral effect with some level of specificity against the herpes virus.

There are conflicting reports concerning its effect on the elevation of blood pressure. Some sources claim that the effect of licorice may be harmful in any amount. Others refute it and state that it has to be consumed in high amounts, such as 3 grams per day for six weeks to significantly elevate blood pressure (I would find it very difficult to consume three grams of licorice as a tea daily for six weeks). Another source claims that even patients with high blood pressure and angina experienced no elevation in their blood pressure when using licorice – provided they were on a low sodium diet.

My impression is that this effect of licorice has not been adequately studied. There are always testimonials and studies claming the opposite. There are more than enough people around us who have benefited from licorice. I like to prescribe it to patients who have low blood pressure, adrenal fatigue and irritated digestive systems. Many of us fit this description.

As with many other herbs, consistent and prolonged use can lead to development of sensitivities.

■ MARJORAM (Origanum majorana)

This herb is similar to its relative wild marjoram (Oreganum vulgare), but with greater effectiveness in settling spasmodic digestion. It is one of the herbs that can be taken pre-emptively to reduce motion sickness.

Our ancestors were also using it as a menstruation promoter.

NUTMEG *(Myristica fragrans)*

This is the only herb in western cooking that could potentially kill. Fortunately, the amount required to produce a deadly effect is more than we would ever use (two whole nutmegs, or more in a meal).

The statement 'medicine in small quantities and poison in larger quantities' applies to this herb. I have never seen or heard of anyone who could tolerate eating enough nutmeg to kill himself or herself. The poisonous effect produced by high amounts of nutmeg manifest initially as stomach pain, dizziness and later followed by stupor.

In small quantities, nutmeg is a digestive aid that can also stop vomiting. It improves appetite and digestive capacities as well as reduces or eliminates gas and bloating. In addition, nutmeg has been very effectively used in herbal formulas for children.

When used for diarrhea, it is specifically effective for those who often feel cold and have chronic 'daybreak diarrhea'. Conversely, nutmeg should be avoided with the hot diarrhea which accompanies dysentery.

Nutmeg is one of the herbs that can produce marijuana-like effects (I have never tested it).

OREGANO *(Origanum vulgare)*

Similar to other Western seasonings, oregano improves digestion by its tonifying and soothing action, reducing gas, spasms and indigestion. Oil of oregano is a more potent form of delivery than the leaves. As expected, it also has the capacity to reduce or relieve menstrual spasms, regulate the menstrual cycle and produce a calming effect.

In addition, it is used for a variety of respiratory illnesses and for coughs because of its expectorant, sweat and fever promoting actions.

Oregano also has anti-parasitic, antiviral and antimicrobial properties, mainly due to its rosmarinic acid content.

In comparison to other herbs in the mint family, oregano tested as having one of the highest antioxidant contents. In general, I prefer to take oregano over many commercial antioxidant preparations. This powerful property may be the reason why oregano was traditionally used to improve various conditions from arthritis to glaucoma.

PARSLEY *(Petroselinum crispum)*

Thanks to its strong diuretic action, parsley is often recommended for patients with high blood pressure and congestive heart failure. Its capacity to reduce the secretion of histamines makes parsley popular for the reduction of allergic reactions.

Season your food with parsley by using the leaves, seeds or juice. Parsley would not be so commonly used in Western cuisine if it wasn't so helpful to our digestion. This herb's carminative actions (carminatives reduce bloating and related pain, gas and flatulence) are also helpful in decreasing PMS-caused bloating and pain. Parsley is also known as a uterine stimulant, helping with difficult menstruation. This is probably due to parsley's antispasmodic properties. It should not be used in pharmaceutical doses in pregnancy.

Sometimes I think that every herb, known or unknown, has been used in the treatment of some cancers. Parsley is no exception. Fresh parsley is also a breath freshener that is high in Vitamins A and C. So, eat those parsley sprigs that you thought were only there as a garnish.

Moderation in everything: high doses of parsley can aggravate the liver, kidneys, digestion, and cause headaches, vertigo or hives.

■ PEPPERMINT *(Menta piperita)*

Peppermint is one of the oldest and most famous digestive herbs. It is an effective digestive aid as well as an antispasmodic and demulcent (soothing) herb. There is evidence demonstrating peppermint's ability to relieve digestive pain and gas as well as prevent stomach ulcers. Peppermint is gentle enough to be used for infant colic. Its added benefit is an ability to promote bile secretion.

As I have said before, if the herb is antispasmodic to the digestive system, it will have the same action on the female reproductive organs. It has been used for morning sickness in pregnancy, but I would not use it if there is a history of miscarriages.

A cup of strong peppermint tea followed by a rest helps with headaches, including migraine headaches accompanied by nausea. This is because peppermint is an anaesthetic (pain relieving) herb. It also may be used topically for pain relief.

Its calming, soothing effect helps with sleep and to reduce coughing. Peppermint is a known decongestant for the respiratory tract, right from the nasal cavity to the bottom of the lungs. This herb's major advantage is that it also has antibacterial and antiviral functions as well as a pleasant taste and smell. Theoretically it can be used to treat cold sores, but lemon balm (Melissa officinalis), another herb from the mint family, is more specific.

■ ROSE HIPS

Hipberries and Rose Flowers have thousands of botanical names such as *Rosa centifolia, Rosa canina, Rosa rugosa, Rosa eglantera, Rosa galica, Rosa roxburghii* and so on. Fresh rose hips are tasty, but cleaning them of their seeds is a bit tedious. In addition to vitamins B, E, K and carotenes, one ounce of rose hips

contains 1000 mg of vitamin C. Our commonly consumed fruits do not even come close.

Unfortunately, we can usually only buy rose hips in a dry form. Drying and subsequent cooking of the hips dramatically reduces the vitamin C content. So, don't expect rosehips or rose-flowers tea bags to provide much vitamin C.

Since there is more to roses than vitamin C, do not hesitate to use them when fighting colds and flus (flowers are often slightly bitter-acidic).

Although some rose species have been used more selectively, as a family, roses have a tremendous variety of medical applications. The primary uses include strengthening of the stomach, heart and nervous system as well as reduction of headaches, earaches, toothaches, sore throats, mouth sores, dizziness and menstrual cramps. Some species have been used as sleep aids, blood cleansers or to relieve indigestion, diarrhea and colic.

My personal opinion is that even if roses had no medicinal benefits, their beauty and aroma are sufficient reason to include them in our cuisine. Both rosehips and flowers are edible.

■ ROSEMARY *(Rosemarinus officinalis)*

Rosemary is a more effective antioxidant than most commercial preparations I am aware of. In addition, it has anti-infective properties independent of those provided by its antioxidant effect. This strong antioxidant property is the reason why people use it to prevent food spoilage.

Similar to other culinary herbs, rosemary is an antispasmodic and digestive aid. Herbs that are antispasmodic to the digestive system usually also have an antispasmodic effect on female organs. When required, rosemary has the capacity to stimulate a sluggish uterus and encourage the menstrual cycle.

Rosemary is an aromatic herb and as such, is a decongestant. This herb is still used in formulas designed to improve memory, prevent arthritis, slow the aging process and reduce wrinkles. There may be some merit to these claims, since rosemary was historically used for improving memory and combating headaches and ringing in the ears. Oriental medicine also uses it to calm the nervous system as well as for stomach pain and headache. One common remedy for headaches is external application of rosemary oil on the affected regions of the head.

I consider rosemary's anti-infective function to be more of an added bonus; I use this herb more for general support and preventative purposes.

SAGE *(Salvia officionalis)*
Sage is known mainly for its astringent (drying) capacity. It can stop milk production, reduce sweating and shrink hemorrhoids. Historically, it was also used to reduce fever and combat infections (canker sores, sore throat, tonsillitis and mastitis). I routinely use it when cooking beans as a digestive aid, antispasmodic and anti-diabetic (reduces blood sugar). It is also a meat preservative – consider sprinkling it on your food when going on a picnic.

Our ancestors tried almost anything to correct problems with the menstrual cycle. Sage is no exception – it has been used as a menstruation promoter since it stimulates the uterus.

Its lesser-known use is for nerve palsy and involuntary shaking.

SAVORY (SUMMER AND WINTER) *(Satureja hortensis and montana)*
In comparison to other herbs in the mint family, savory is considered less potent. For this reason it is frequently prescribed for children. It has been used to help with lack of appetite, indigestion, diarrhea and other digestive problems. Since it's an expectorant, it can be used to expel phlegm. Savory tea has been used as a gargle to relieve sore throat. It is also prized for its capacity to reduce gas produced by beans consumption.

STINGING NETTLES *(Urtica doica)*
Nettles have been used to strengthen the entire body. This is a very versatile herb often described as a 'nourishing diuretic' because of its high vitamin and mineral content in addition to its effective diuretic action. No wonder our ancestors used nettles to treat congestive heart failure and high blood pressure.

In general, people have used nettles to treat a variety of urinary tract problems and stinging pain. Stinging nettles are an effective kidney purifier, improving the elimination of uric acid via urine. In addition, nettles improve elimination of solid wastes via the skin and bowel.

Current research also supports the traditional use and effectiveness of nettles in the treatment of hay fever, asthma, allergies and sensitivities. Native women drank nettle tea during pregnancy to strengthen the fetus. Additional historic uses include treatment and prevention of scurvy. My ancestors used it to treat and prevent arthritis.

Nettles can be used internally and externally. When used in cooking, focus on young leaves only, such as the top three rows of leaves before the top flower. Wilt the leaves as you do when cooking spinach and keep the lid off the pot to allow the oxalic acid to evaporate.

Dry nettles do not sting, fresh ones do. However, I do not use any gloves when harvesting them. According to old herbalists, if you are 'brave and gentle' they will not sting you. Unless you have an allergic reaction to it, being stung by nettles is actually one way to use them externally – such as for the treatment of arthritis.

Nettles are used to decrease prostate-related hormonal binding as well as to reduce and prevent prostatic hyperplasia, (enlargement of the prostate). They can be used to stop internal and external bleeding, such as blood in the urine, hemorrhoids or to regulate excessive menstrual flow.

Nettles have a high amount of iron, which is specifically important to those who do not consume meat. Lesser known uses for nettles are the treatment of vaginal infections and the reduction of blood glucose levels. Apart from the famous nettle tea, nettles were also added to stuffing. As expected, some people successfully figured out how to make wine and beer from nettles.

■ TARRAGON *(Artemisia dracunculus)*

Tarragon does exactly what is expected of culinary herbs. It improves appetite, digestive disorders and pain, promotes urination and menstruation and reduces insomnia. It has anesthetic properties for the same reason as cloves and allspice. Tarragon is also antimicrobial. Unfortunately, its active ingredients tend to evaporate quickly, so if it doesn't have much of an aroma, it isn't fresh and will not be as potent.

■ THYME *(Thymus vulgaris)*

Thyme can do much more than taste good, smell good and look good. It is a highly efficient antibacterial, antifungal and antiseptic herb. In fact, it was used as one of the original antiseptic agents in locations where first aid and medical aid was provided. Even in our modern times it is an ingredient in Listerine® mouthwash.

Thyme is an effective expectorant that also strengthens lungs. Thyme has been used to help cure almost anything related to the upper respiratory airways and lungs: sore throat, laryngitis, cough, whooping cough and others. An ancient teaching states: "Thyme is to the trachea and bronchi what peppermint is to the stomach."

Like other culinary herbs, thyme has an antispasmodic effect on the smooth muscles of the gastrointestinal system and uterus. Some Naturopaths are using it in women's formulas to promote the menstrual cycle. It is also used for indigestion and nervousness.

Thyme is obviously safe to use in cooking as a seasoning. Bear in mind that the distillates or oils are more powerful than the dried herb.

■ TURMERIC *(Curcuma longa, Curcuma domestica)*

Turmeric has been used in medicine for at least as long as *Ginkgo biloba*.

Turmeric is an antibacterial and antiparasitic herb which is always handy in our kitchen cabinet. Just apply it on the wound (it doesn't hurt) or spray it over the food as long as it is compatible with the other seasonings. In some cultures, turmeric has been used for the treatment of dysentery.

It is one of my favourite mild, liver-protecting herbs. Turmeric reduces the toxic effect of various medications and other toxins on the liver. It can be called upon any time we need to improve liver conditions, illnesses and liver function. We can also use it to increase bile production. Among other roles, bile helps us emulsify (digest) fats and detoxify.

However, turmeric gained the most fame in the treatment of arthritis. In fact, it has anti-inflammatory effects that are comparable to phenylbutazone.

Since it reduces blood clotting and blood cholesterol, it has been used as a cardiovascular system-protecting herb.

Literature also states that it has been used for tumor prevention and inhibition of lymphoma.

There might be some merit to this since turmeric supports the main organs, such as the liver. Many Naturopathic doctors may recall the saying, "Cancer begins in the liver".

■ USNEA *(Various species, also known as Old Man's Beard, Usno, Binan or San-lo)*

Usnea is a parasitic lichen growing on either dead or living trees. It is widespread and prefers primarily conifers in a damp environment. However, do not look for it in your grocery store. North American Indians used it as a food to such an extent that they would even declare ownership of specific trees covered with usnea. They were also known to chop such trees down so they could collect the usnea more effectively.

The plant has to be cooked to be digestible. Medicinal qualities include antifungal, antimicrobial, antiviral and antibiotic actions. When consumed cooked, it does not irritate the digestion. In fact, it has a relaxing effect on our smooth muscles similar to that of papaverine, found in poppy seeds. Apart from its use as a food source, it has been used to treat infections affecting almost any organ or bodily system including the respiratory, digestive, urinary, reproductive and skin systems.

It has a mild mushroom-like taste with a bit of a peppery edge. My preference is to cook it with grains for the same amount of time as the grain. Other people prefer to cook it for a few minutes only. It is difficult to advise on the amount to use. Any amount, from a few strands to a fistful, is acceptable. Use it as the only seasoning or in combination with other wild or culinary herbs, such as marjoram or thyme. Usnea may also be used as a replacement for garlic in cooking. I have observed that every time I cook with usnea, I use less salt.

■ DANDELION *(Taraxicum officionalis)*

I can't resist, but I have to mention dandelions. I would place this herb ahead of any other herb in terms of its usefulness in our highly industrialized society; this includes Ginseng and Gingko.

Dandelions are the fourth most nutrient rich, green vegetable (ninth when compared to all vegetables, grains and seeds). They contain more iron than spinach and more carotenoids and vitamin A than carrots. Dandelions are used as vegetables or made into wine, beer, or coffee. Their flowers are great in cakes and pancakes. Dried or roasted roots make a tasty, low calorie snack, replacing nuts or seeds.

Dandelions have many therapeutic effects. They are a more effective diuretic than *Lasix (Furosemide)*, improve production of bile (fat digestion and detoxification), are effective in the treatment and prevention of liver disorders, provide blood glucose balancing effects, exhibit mild laxative effects when required, improve appetite and strengthen the gastrointestinal system. Dandelions are used in an impressive spectrum of conditions from menstrual abnormalities to arthritis and elevated cholesterol. Introduce them gradually.

SUBSTITUTING FRESH AND DRIED HERBS

2 t. fresh herbs = 1 t. crumbled dry herbs or ¼ t. powdered dry herbs.

CONCERNING SEASONING

- *The softer the more finely ground it is, the later it is added to your cooking.*
  - *Whole spices, such as peppercorns, can be added in the initial stage of cooking because they will release their flavours slowly. This includes bay leaves. These are best simmered for longer periods, then removed before food is served.*
  - *Ground, hard spices (often colourful), are added in the last 10 to 15 minutes of cooking*
  - *Green herbs are added even later so their flavour will not evaporate.*
- *May be added to butter or oil that will be used for cooking or will be poured over the finished food.*
  - *Just mix the spices into the butter or oil, cover and let stand to disperse the flavours over time.*
- *Can be used for marinating which can take anywhere from several hours to overnight to several days.*
- *If the preparation calls for a very quick cooking time, rub the seasonings into the food before cooking. This method is great for braising, stir-frying, quick-steaming, broiling, and frying.*
- *To activate or release more flavour from the herbs or spices, crush them between your fingers or between two spoons – a mortar and pestle is ideal for this.*
- *To save time, you can also make blends of your favourite spices and store them in separate containers. However, do not forget to rotate the spices.*

DELICIOUS SEASONING COMBINATIONS

MILD BLENDS:
- basil, bay leaf, oregano, parsley
- basil, marjoram, rosemary, thyme
- basil, celery, parsley
- anise, fennel, sage, savory

WARMING, MORE PUNGENT BLENDS:
- chili, coriander, cumin
- curry, garlic, ginger, turmeric
- paprika, pepper

SWEET BLENDS:
- allspice, anise, cinnamon, cloves
- ginger, cardamom, nutmeg

FOODS AND THE SEASONINGS THAT LOVE THEM

Beef, Chicken, Lamb:
basil, chili peppers, caraway, cinnamon, coriander, cumin, curry, garlic, ginger, marjoram, lemon, oregano, paprika, parsley, pepper, rosemary, sage, tarragon, turmeric, thyme (or almost any other seasoning)

Eggs:
basil, chili peppers, curry, dill, fennel, garlic, ginger, paprika, rosemary, sage, savory, tarragon, thyme

Fish:
anise, basil, bay leaf, caraway seeds, coriander, curry, dill, fennel, garlic, ginger, lemon, oregano, paprika, parsley, pepper, rosemary, sage, thyme

Amaranth, Buckwheat, Oat, Quinoa, Rye, Basil:
Caraway seeds, celery seeds, marjoram, parsley, rosemary, sage

Rice, Millet, Oats:
almost any seasoning

Bread:
anise, basil, caraway, cardamom, cinnamon, coriander, cumin, dill, garlic, oregano, rosemary, sage, thyme

Beans, Lentils, Peas:
allspice, basil, bay leaf, cayenne, celery seed, chili peppers, cloves, cumin, parsley, pepper, sage, savory, thyme

Broccoli, Brussels Sprouts, Cabbage, Cauliflower, Kohlrabi:
caraway seed, celery, dill, garlic, onion, pepper

Bok Choy, Savoy Cabbage and Green Leafy Vegetables:
dill, garlic, marjoram, nutmeg, oregano, parsley, rosemary, thyme

Carrots, Squash:
allspice, anise, basil, cardamom, cinnamon, cloves, curry powder, fennel, ginger, mint, nutmeg, parsley, rosemary, thyme

Cucumber, Zucchini:
basil, chives, coriander, cumin, curry, dill, oregano, parsley, pepper, turmeric

Jicama, Daikon, Parsnips, Rutabaga, Squash, Turnips:
allspice, basil, cinnamon, cloves, dill, ginger, marjoram, nutmeg, oregano, paprika, parsley, pepper, rosemary

Beets or Fruit:
allspice, anise, basil, cardamom, cinnamon, cloves, curry, fennel, ginger, mint, nutmeg, rosemary

STORING SEASONINGS

Culinary herbs and spices need to be stored in a dry environment in airtight containers. Containers of amber glass or stainless steel are preferable; at the very least cover them to protect them from light. Storage temperature should be lower than 70°F and should not widely fluctuate.

45

Every state, province and city has its favourite locales for healthier foods. Exploring these is beyond the scope of this book.

Consider the following:
Contact Naturopathic physicians in your area. They will most likely know where, what and with whom to deal. Most likely they will also know the good and bad about various vendors, growers and ranchers.

Contact your local association of organic growers and enquire about their member list. Find out specifically how organic their products are, as well as where, what and how to buy from them.

Beware:
Inquire about the regulation of organic growers in your area. There are considerable differences between different organic associations; some associations allow food that is substantially less organic than others.

In addition, free-range does not necessarily mean that the animals are roaming free. It may mean that they simply have access to a free roaming area, if they can get to it. For example, a chicken kept in a barn might not have the capacity to walk out of the barn, yet it can be slaughtered and labeled as free-range organic. Other free-range producers may have livestock freely roaming in a very natural setting. Find out who's who.

I prefer to buy food from smaller local organic producers. However, since I live in a major Canadian city which happens to have a very short growing season, I also have to buy imported organic products from major organic growers located in the U.S.

There are multiple options open to us:

Note:

There is a substantial variation in quality of organic food.

FARMERS' MARKETS:

General advantages:
- Local, fresher food
- More emphasis on food that is in season
- Opportunity to meet the grower/rancher

General disadvantages:
- Sells imported food alongside local fare
- Beware – a vendor may have less at stake than a store owner
- Subject to seasonal availability

HEALTH FOOD STORES

General advantages:
- Sell organic or naturally produced foods
- Can be price-competitive with some conventionally produced foods
- Greater variety of organic and health food
- Focus on providing healthier alternatives

General disadvantages:
- Can't always determine sincerity of their claims
- Might or might not verify the origin of the food they sell
- Sometimes can't compete on price with conventionally grown foods
- Depending on popularity, potentially lower turnover, e.g. less-fresh produce

HEALTH FOOD SECTION IN CONVENTIONAL STORES

General advantages:
- Proximity/convenience

General disadvantages:
- Less selection
- Might have large suppliers but not necessarily those with the best products
- Might have lesser variety and lower turnover, e.g. older produce
- These stores usually cater to people looking for fresher appearing, cheaper produce

which is grown to be large and "attractive" as opposed to being more nutritious and organic
- Some carry organic products more for the promotional effect, or to test the market, rather than for viable profit

ORGANIC FOOD CO-OPS

General advantages:
- Quite good if well operated and stable
- Easy to set up (group a number of people together who want organic food and have the growers or distributors drop off bulk quantities at one person's location).
- Co-op can be virtually any size and still save you money
- Potential to develop into a storefront or a chain of stores
- Easy and inexpensive to go out of business if it does not work out
- Make some like-minded friends and maybe even meet the person of your dreams

General disadvantages:
- A mess if not well run or if some members contribute more aggravation than support
- Potential to lose some of your friends

ORGANIC FOOD CO-OPS ASSOCIATED WITH A FARM AND/OR SELECTED GROWERS/RANCHERS

General advantages:
- Local, seasonal food, grown in conditions of which you approve
- Food is often harvested in the morning and delivered to you in the afternoon
- An opportunity to contribute your labour and physically participate in food distribution and/or production
- Be involved in decision-making concerning food production
- See the impact of your work and forces of nature on food production success or failure

- Be a part of the concerned community and meet people who resonate with you
- An opportunity to get together with other members, for a day or an afternoon at the farm to work, cook, eat and socialise
- Simply pay your financial contribution and just receive your share of food delivery

General disadvantages:
- Same as the above listed advantages
- Memberships may be limited and you might not get in as a member on the first try

TO-YOUR-DOOR ORGANIC FOOD DELIVERY

General advantages:
- Fresher food if well managed
- Delivered to your door

General disadvantages:
- Older food if not managed well
- Less selection
- May be more expensive

PERSONAL CONTACT WITH THOSE WHO PRODUCE BETTER AND CLEANER FOOD

General advantages:
- Fresher food as available
- Food may be highly superior to that of large producers
- You can get to know who feeds you
- Supporting "the little guys", their animals and the land
- Greater connection with the land and food

General disadvantages:
- Limited selection
- Less convenient
- Nature dependent
- Freezer required if you consume meat

"When our son Brandon was two years old he was diagnosed with idiopathic acute recurrent pancreatis. Brandon suffered five severe attacks all within one year requiring hospitalization, morphine, antibiotics, and TPN (total parental nutrition) by IV. During the first attack, we almost lost him.

This really took a great physical toll on him but as a parent you cannot accept that you are unable to help your child and, as much as we tried to remain hopeful, our emotions began spiraling into helplessness. We needed a light at the end of the tunnel and once we met and began working with Dr. Kodet we knew that was exactly what we had found.

Dr. Kodet is not only extremely knowledgeable, but is also very caring and has the ability to explain the intricate workings of the body to the layman. He suggested Brandon eat a very specific hypoallergenic diet. Our diet always had consisted of a wide variety of healthy foods and our children did not eat junk foods, but we were naive to everyday foods which may have been contributing to Brandon's symptoms. Thus a turning point began and even within the first week following Dr. Kodet's dietary recommendations, we noticed a marked improvement in Brandon's energy.

Brandon has since had a handful of comparatively mild episodes which appeared to be symptomatically related to the pancreas (but nothing requiring hospitalization) and has been a great deal healthier since following Dr. Kodet's diet for almost four years now! We will always feel grateful to have met Dr. Kodet and quite honestly feel he very well may have saved Brandon."

– Brandon Ward

BIBLIOGRAPHY

Atkins, Robert C. *Atkins' New Diet Revolution.*
New York: HarperCollins, 2001.

Atkins, Robert C. *Atkins For Life.*
New York: St. Martin's Press, 2004.

MacDonald, SIdney, Baker. *Detoxification and Healing.*
New York, McGraw-Hill, 2003.

Bennett, Peter and Barrie, Stephen. *7-Day Detox Miracle.*
New York: Crown Publishing Group, 2001.

Chopra, Deepak. *Perfect Health.*
New York: Crown Publishing Group, 1991.

Cordain, Loren. *The Paleo Diet.*
New York: John Wiley & Sons, 2002.

Crook, William C. and Cynthia P. and Carol Jessop.
Chronic Fatigue Syndrome and the Yeast Connection.
New York: Professional Books Inc., 1992.

Crook, William C. and James H. Brodsky. *The Yeast Connection: A Medical Breakthrough.*
New York: Vintage Books: 1986.

Dhonden, Yeshi. *Healing from the Source: The Science and Lore of Tibetan Medicine.*
New York: Snow Lion Publications, 2000.

Duke, James A. *The Green Pharmacy: The Ultimate Compendium of Natural Remedies
from the World's Foremost Authority on Healing Herbs.*
New York: St. Martin's Press, 2000.

Flaws, Bob. *Scatology and the Gate of Life: The Role of the Large Intestine in Immunity,
an Integrated Chinese-Western Approach.*
New York: Blue Poppy Press, 1990.

Fredericks, Carlton and Herman Goodman. *Low Blood Sugar and You.*
New York: Grosset & Dunlap, 1969.

Hope-Murray, Angela and Tony Pickup. *Discover Ayurveda.*
Berkley: Ulysses Press, 1998.

Krishna, Subhadra. *Esssential Ayurveda.*
Novato: New World Library, 2005.

Kushi, Avaline and Maya Tiwari and Wendy Esko. *Diet for Natural Beauty.*
Tokyo: Japan Publications, 1991.

Kushi, Michio and Alex Jack. *The Macrobiotic Path To Total Health.*
New York: Ballantine Books, 2003

Lu, Henry C. *Chinese Natural Cures: Traditional Methods for Remedy and Prevention.*
New York: Black Dog & Leventhal, Inc., 2006.

Lust, J. *The Herb Book.*
New York: Bantam Books, 2003.

Maciocia,G., *The Foundations of Chinese Medicine, a Comprehensive Text*
New York: Elsevier Health Sciences, 2005.

Matsen, John and Irene Hayton and Carol Song.
Eating Alive II, Ten Easy Steps to Following the Eating Alive System.
Vancouver: Goodwin Books, 2002.

Mentha, M. *Health Through Yoga.*
London: HarperCollins Publishers, 2002.

Mercola, Joseph and Alison Rose Levy. *The No-Grain Diet.*
New York: Plume, 2004.

Mitchell, W.A. *Plant Medicine in Practice.*
St. Louis: Churchill Livingstone, 11830 Westline Industrial Drive, St.Louis, Missouri 63146, 2003

Murray, Michael T. and Joseph Pizzorno. *Encyclopedia of Natural Medicine.*
Rocklin: Prima Publishing, 1991.

Muramoto, Naboru and Michel Abehsera.
Healing Ourselves: A Book to Serve as a Companion in Time of Illness and Health.
New York: Avon Books, 1977.

Piazza, Gail. *World of Wok Cookery.* Boston: Dorison House Publishers, 1982.

Sandifer, Jon and Bob Lloyd. *Macrobiotics For Beginners.*
London: Piatkus Books, 2000.

Schmid, Ronald F. *Traditional Foods Are Your Best Medicine.*
New York: Healing Arts Press, 1997.

Schwartzbein, Diana. *The Schwartzbein Principle*.
Deerfield Beach: Health Communications, Inc., 1999.

Sears, Barry. *Enter The Zone*.
New York: HarperCollins Publishers, Inc., 1995.

Sears, Barry. *Mastering The Zone*.
New York: ReganBooks, Inc., 1997.

Sears, Barry. *Omega Rx Zone*.
New York: Collins Living Publishers Inc., 2003.

Svoboda, Robert E. *Ayurveda for Women*.
New York: Healing Arts Press, 2000.

Thom, Dick. *Coping with Food Intolerances*.
New York: Sterling Publishing Company, Inc., 2002.

Trowbridge, John Parks and Morton Walker. *The Yeast Syndrome*.
New York: Bantam Books, 1986.

Willard, Terry. *Text Book of Advanced Herbology*.
Calgary: Wild Rose College of Natural Healing, Ltd., 1992.

Willard, Terry. *Text Book of Modern Herbology*.
Calgary: Wild Rose College of Natural Healing, Ltd., 1993.

Williams, T. *Chinese Medicine*.
London: HarperCollins Publishers, 77-85 Fulham Palace Rd. Hammersmith, London W6 8JB

Yance, Donald. *Herbal Medicine, Healing and Cancer*.
Chicago: McGraw-Hill, 1999.

Young, J. *Eastern Healing*.
London: Duncan Baird Publishers Ltd. 75-76 Wells Str., London W1T 3QH

INDEX

breakfast, 55-56

buckwheat, 29, 33-6, 39-40, 42-45, 57, **82-85**, **87-88**, 90, **92-93**, 97, 99,**101**, 103-104, 106, 119, 122-123, 126, 128, **133**-4, 150, 161 163-4, 181

buffalo, 40, 44

butter from seeds, **68**, 31, 42-44, 57, 73, 96, 102-103, 110, 125, 129, 136, 141 nuts, 34, 57, 61, 65, **67**-68, 91, 128, 130, 147

C

cake, 6, 35, 56, 79, 84, 103, 109, 179

caraway seeds, 168, 181

cardamom, 169, 181

cayenne, 169, 181

celery seeds, 169, 181

celiac patients, **45**-46

chamomile, 169, 181

chews, 108

chicken, 11, 23, 29, 33, 40, 43-44, 56, 75-76, 78, 116-120, 123-124, 126, 130, 134, 149, 156, 160, 180, 182

children's formulas, 61

chilly pepper, 169, 181

chocolate, **26, 33, 38**, 60,

cilantro, 170, 181

cinnamon, 170, 181

clarified butter (ghee), 38

cleaning cooking items, **49**-50, 52, 156, 176

cloves, 170, 181

coffee, 26, 31, **33, 59**, 89, 170-171, 179,

coffee substitutes, 33, 59, 89

cookies, 36, 104-105,

cookware, 47-48

contamination, 13, 48, **51-52**

coriander, 170, 181

crackers, 34, 35, 43-44, **83**, 56-58, 74-76, 82-83, 91, 141, 166

crepes, 56-57, 83, 90, 109, 166

cross contamination prevention, 13, 48, **51-53**

D

dandelions, 179

dill, 171

dips, 73

diversified diet, 10

diversify – diversify food choices, 28-39

dressings, 70-72

duck, 29, 33, 42, 44, 156

dumplings, 109, 110

E

elimination diet, 10

F

fats, XII, 14, 17, **26**, 31, **53**, 58, 61-2, 69, 108
fennel, 171
fermented soy products, 32, 39
fish, 8, 11, 17, 26-29, 31, 41, 43-44, 49, 51-53, 56-58, 61, 71, **117**, **124**, 129, 141, 158, **162-164**
food diary, 22, 25, 27-28, **40-41**, 45, 83
foods to avoid, see avoid
fruits, 12,14, 26-27, 31-32, 37, 44, 52, 56-57, 59, 62, 86, 91, 107, **109**, 128, 176
fun, 166
fundamentals – fundamentals of my nutritional approach, 10

G

garlic, 172,
garlic oil, 70-71
ginger, 172
gingerbread, 103
gluten, 35, 45-47, 111
goose, 29, 43-44
grains, Xii, Xiii, 11-12, 16, **26**, 28-**29**, 33, 36, 39-41, 52, 55-57, 71, 74, 76-78, **81-107**, 115-116, 118, 121, 123, 126, **127-137**, **142**, 154, 160-161, 166, **181**
granola, 108
grouse, 29

H

heart, 44, 116, 156, 159-160, 169, 171, 173, 175-7
herbs and spices hot list, 180
herbs in the kitchen, 167
hops, 173
hypoallergenic diet, 10

J

juicing, 14

K

kidneys, 3, 13, 15, 26, 33, **115**, **123**, **159**-161, 168, 175, 177

L

lama, 29, 44
lamb, 11, 29, 40, 42-44, 77, 115-116, 121, 126, 150, 152, 156, 180
licorice, 172
liver, 3, 15,73, 75, 159-161, 175, 178-179
liver pâté, 73, 75

P

prevention, 4, 52, 172, 177, 179

purée, **44**, 61-62, 74, 77, 79, 112-123, 118, 120-123, 118, **120**-125

Q

quick meals, 55-56

quinoa, **29**, **33- 35**, 39-40, 42-43, 56-57, **62-64**, 83, **85**, **95**, **97**, 101, **115**, 126, **135-136**

R

raw impact, 12, 14, 47, 52, 59, 70-71, 77, 125, 129, 145, 153

recommendations - key recommendations, 26

recommended foods hot-lists, 29

reference list – Quick Reference List, 26

        animal protein - meat, fish, poultry, venison, 39

        beans/lentils, 29

        grains, 29

        vegetables, 30

        sea vegetables, 30, 39

        seeds and nuts and their butters, 30

        oils and fats, 31

        beverages, 31

        fermented soy products, 32, 39

        sweets and sugar replacements, 31

        fruits, 32

        berries, 32

rice, 23, 29, 31-36, 39-40, 42-44, 48-56, 59-62-66, 68-69, 77-79, 82, 84-**85**, 87, **89-92-93**-95, **97**-98, **101**-113, **116**, **118-119**, 123-124, 126-134, 136-137, 152-155,163-164, 166

roasting, 30, 51, 67, 108, 149, 151,164

rose hips, 174

rosemary, 174

rotate your foods, 10, 19, 25, 27, 30, **40**-41, 180

rotation - four-day rotation example, **40**-44

rotational diet, 10

rye, 29, 33-35, 40, 42-45, 56, 83, **99**, **100**, 127-128, **132**-133, 151 160, **181**

S

safer food handling, 16, 47, **50**-51, 56, 70, 127, 167

safer food handling (vegetables), 143

safer food handling (fruits), 109

slow cooking, **16**, 23, 56, 58, **67**, **129**, 147, 152, 158, 180

storing, 50, 52, 54, **181**,

sage, 177

salads, 12, 43, 71, 134, **140-141**, **145-6**

salad - wilted, 145-146

sandwich fillings, 44, 73, 76

U

usnea, 179
utensils-cooking, 47-49, 50, 52, 52-53,155

V

vegetables, 10-14, 16, 22-23, 26, 28, **30**, 39, 40, 44, 52, 56-58, 71, 74-75, 77-**81**-82, 88-89, 94, 99, 100-111, 114, 137, 141, 152, 157, 161-**164**, 166, 179, 181
venison, 11, 29, 40, 44

W

wheat, 6, 10, 22, 26, 33, **35-36**, 45, 57, 93, 95, 100, **127-128**, 166
wheat flour substitute, 35
wheat substitutes, 29, 34

The List of Crash Courses

Abbreviations
c. = cup
T. = Tablespoon
t. = teaspoon
g. = gram